Teen Interactive

First Edition

Greater Than my MOOD

Complete Guide for
Anger, Anger Management, Bullying
Conflict Resolution & Self-Control
Workbook

Ramona Girley, PMHNP

The publisher and the author are providing the content of this
book is for informational purposes only and is not intended
to diagnose, treat, cure, or prevent any condition or disease.
You understand that this book is not intended as a substitute
for consultation with a licensed practitioner. Please consult
with your own physician or healthcare specialist regarding the
suggestions and recommendations made in this book. The use
of this book implies your acceptance of this disclaimer.

Gemlight Publishing LLC
45 Hardy Court Shopping Ctr, #385
Gulfport MS,39507
www.gemlightpublishingllc@gmail.com

Ordering Information:
Quantity sales. Special discounts are available on quantity
purchases by corporations, associations, and others.
For details, contact the publisher at the address above.
Orders by U.S. trade bookstores and wholesalers.
Please contact Big Distribution: Tel: (833) 436-5483;
or email gemlightpublishingllc@gmail.com

Printed in the United States of America

First Edition ISBN#978-17344326-8-8 (Perfect Bound)

First Edition

Greater Than my MOOD

Complete Guide for
Anger, Anger Management, Bullying
Conflict Resolution & Self-Control
Workbook

Ramona Girley, PMHNP

GEMLIGHT PUBLISHING LLC.

Gulfport, Mississippi

ACKNOWLEDGEMENTS

To my children, (Tiamber, Robyn, Rachel, and Trey), my greatest inspiration for writing this workbook. Life during "YOUR" teen years threw some hard punches, but through it all, "YOU" made it.

My grandchildren Dra & RJ, Nana loves you very much.

Special Thanks:

My husband (Travis) for your support and reading all the many drafts even when you didn't want to.

My sister (Kim) my number one cheerleader who makes me think I can walk to the moon and back without a space shuttle with her pep rallies designed for me!

My mom (Martha), who's strength has encouraged me and gave me "my" strength to accomplish the things I have done today without you, there would be no me.

My Dad (George), thanks for your support and encouragement.

To all the teens who have attended RG MindfulHealth 4 OUR Youth who gave me positive feedback and told me they would buy my books, Thanks!

I couldn't name everyone but know that I am thankful to everyone who has supported and encouraged me.

CONTENTS

Hello,

My name is Ramona Girley. I am a Mental health nurse practitioner with a passion for helping youth develop coping skills in sensitive areas that are difficult to share or discuss with others. I can say I know this to be true because two of my four children were bullied in middle and high school, and they did not inform me until well after the fact. One of my children had stated, "I did not want you to worry!" I did not find out until she was an adult. My other child, I found out while he was in school, but he did not tell me either, stating, " because a girl did it!"

This workbook was designed to

- Give you informative information.

- Provide you with interactive, reflective questions to explore your thoughts, feelings, and behaviors.

- Identify feelings that may be challenging.

- Explore strategies for managing challenging feelings.

- Apply and practice the strategies that you will learn.

This is the first series, and I decided to start with the **ABC'S... Anger, Anger Management, Bullying, Conflict Resolutions**, and **Self-Control**. Why?

These subjects have become the main problems that happen all over the world. **Anger and Bullying** affect many different things: people, work, self-esteem, self-love, physical and mental health. These effects can last a long time and can cause learning problems while at school, as well as difficulty in creating and maintaining prosocial relationships with friends and family.

How many times have you heard, "Sticks and stones may break my bones, but words will never hurt me."? Well, this is FALSE! Words do hurt, and sometimes hurt more than someone physically hitting you.

Words can stay with you for a long time, causing **Anger**, hurt, resentment, and feelings of abandonment, making you feel like you are not good enough. The lists go on and on. Hurtful words are an example of an emotional scar that is not visible to others but will last for a lifetime, causing physical and psychological damage.

Bullying can occur at home, school, work, and anywhere. Guess what, Bullying can even happen with adults. That is why it is so important to discuss Bullying, its effects, how it affects people, and how we can STOP it while you are still in the developmental phases of your teenage years!

I will also discuss **Conflict Resolutions** and give you some coping skills on how to deal with bullying or help someone who is bullied. These coping skills discussed within this workbook are skills you can use now, and by the time you are an adult, you will be prepared.

The best part about this workbook is that it is interactive, and I encourage you to be honest with your answers. Make it YOURS! There is no right or wrong answer. I know personally how the "lasting" effects of bullying can stay with a person because I witnessed how my children were affected physically and emotionally.

Bullying is not only a severe problem at school, and it is a critical problem for society at large.

After reading and engaging in this workbook, you will discover that it is designed to help you learn practical life skills to make it a part of your daily routine. You will learn how to achieve several things; decrease anger levels, especially in confrontational situations, the useful tips for you to control Anger and not let anger control you, and how to understand and implement ways to control Anger to resolve conflicts for your continued growth in the future.

I hope that you will infuse every word, daily exercises, statements and apply them to your life. There is nothing more fulfilling than being "Greater" than your state of mind of feeling or let say "MOOD." With a little boost and encouragement, you on your way to enjoyable adolescent years!

Ramona,

Section 1

Anger

"For every minute you remain angry, you give up sixty seconds of peace of mind."

Ralph Waldo Emerson

1.1 What is Anger?

Anger is an emotional response that we have to an external (outside) or internal (inside) event that we have perceives as a threat or injustice.

Anger is a natural, healthy human emotion that everyone has, at some point, from feelings of irritation, disapproval, to annoyance. Yes, I did say "healthy." Anger happens whether we want it to or not, and everyone experiences anger at some point in their life. Anger is tied to our natural survival instinct of protecting our self from what is perceived from a feeling of wrongdoing.

Anger can be a primary or secondary emotion. Secondary Anger occurs when another emotion happens first. For example, after feelings of sadness about something, you then become angry. Knowing this will be helpful when you are identifying triggers/root causes and picking what coping skills that need to apply to "that" situation.

Anger does not always create a negative situation or a negative experience. Anger is healthy because sometimes we need Anger to manage certain situations in our life. What makes Anger become such a "bad" word/situation is what we do when we get angry (our behavior.)

Different Intensity Levels of Anger

- Mild
- Moderate
- Extreme/Severe.

The definition of anger varies depending on whom you ask, just as the cause does. Different things make people angry. The same thing that makes me angry does not make my sister angry.

Verbal-spoken out loud

- Shouting
- Threats
- Ridicule
- Sarcasm
- Blame
- Criticism.

Nonverbal- not spoken, but visibly seen

- Frowning
- Clenching fist
- Pointing
- Folding arms across the chest
- Turning back while someone is talking to you.

Situational Factors that can Cause Feelings of Anger:

- Stress
- Basic needs unmet (food, shelter, sleep, etc.)
- Change
- Different beliefs/opinion/values
- Ineffective communication.

Why Does Anger Feel Good?

- Anger empowers
- Anger energizes
- Gives a sense of security (sometimes false.)

Describe in detail a specific situation that made you angry. Was it resolved? Why or why not?

Healthy Anger

I wanted to talk about this because anger gets such a bad name all the time. It's frown upon, but anger is necessary for certain parts of our daily life to function correctly.

When anger is appropriate to the situation, and it is not used to punish, hurt, intimidate, control, manipulate, or get back at someone, then it is healthy. Healthy anger is when it is expressed in a way to allow feelings and opinions to cage unfair situations or solve problems.

It is socially appropriate to acknowledge when something upsets you, or you feel threatened. The problem occurs when the acknowledgment is done in an unhealthy, inappropriate manner (discussed in more detail in the anger management section.)

Healthy roles of anger (in moderation with coping skills):

- When anger signals you that you are frustrated or annoyed
- Acts as an energizer enable you to deal with conflict problems
- Prompts you to communicate with others
- Creates a sense of control and allow you to be more assertive.

Unhealthy Anger

Used with the intent of punishing, hurting, or getting back at someone in a destructive way. Often done with high intensity and may include yelling, sulking, manipulation, blackmail, silent treatments, or threats. Anger is often held in until it explodes.

How Unhealthy roles of anger (lack of coping skills) affects your body:

- Disrupts your thoughts and makes it difficult to think clearly
- Makes it easy to avoid other feelings like sadness, anxiety, or embarrassment
- Too much can lead to aggression
- Affects relationships (ineffective communication)
- Physical/Mental Health problems (Depression, High Blood Pressure, Headache.)

Myths About Anger

- Ignore it, and it will go away
- Let it out, and you will feel better (burst)
- If I am not angry, others will walk all over me
- I cannot help it; I am an angry person
- It is not my fault (people did this to me.)

Things that Cause us to Become Angry

- Events
- Experiences
- Thoughts
- Feelings
- Attitudes
- Our behavior.

Two Common Underlying Causes of Anger

- Fear
- Pain.

However, these two emotions are broad and cover many things.

Fear can be physical or psychological. Fear of being laughed at, fear of abandonment, even fear of being unloved.

Pain is more than physically hurt. Pain also comes from emotional and psychological causes, feeling pain from the loss of love, feeling pain because of life's unfairness, or pain from losing things.

Can You Control Your Anger?

Yes, you absolutely can. The first thing you must do is recognize what makes you angry. Awareness is one of the most helpful tools that we have for keeping our anger under control. In addition to recognizing what made you angry, pay attention to the physical symptoms that your anger is building up. For example, clenching your teeth/fists, increased heart rate, and increased breathing.

Ask Yourself

- Why am I angry?
- Is it one factor or multiple factors causing me to be angry?
- Is my anger caused by a "feeling" or "situation"?
- Is my anger justified? Are you angry because you do not want to compromise, or you are not getting your way? This is known as the displacement of anger. To displace anger means we take out our angry feelings on someone or something that has nothing to do with the source of our anger.

Why is it Important to Recognize What Makes You Angry?

Once you have identified the things that make you angry, it is important that you know that your thoughts play a significant role in your anger processing. Angry thoughts automatically pop in our minds, and we cannot control that, but we can control how we respond to these thoughts.

Anger is a learned behavior repeated from what we have seen in our homes, and the way our family/friends respond to things that make them angry. Since how we respond to anger is learned, that means we can unlearn the bad behaviors and learn new responses to anger. But to change, you must want to.

This workbook is designed to help you learn and understand more about anger in a general sense and coping skills that will help you to manage and control your response to anger in a healthy, productive manner.

Anger has been compared to and called an umbrella emotion. Why? Because anger can cover many emotions/feelings. Learn to recognize the underlying emotion and relationship of the emotion you are experiencing when you are angry. Why? Because anger is a protective emotion that can be useful and positive to you.

Feelings/Emotions that are the Underlying Reasons/ Causes of Anger:

- Rejection/hurt
- Fear
- Embarrassment
- Insecurity
- Need to be perfect

- Feelings of unloved/misunderstood
- Helpless
- Hurt by criticism
- Tired (mentally and physically exhausted.)

List one or two feelings that you can identify that has been something that has caused you to become angry. Describe the situation. What was the outcome?

_____

_____

_____

_____

_____

_____

_____

_____

_____

_____

_____

_____

_____

_____

_____

_____

_____

_____

_____

_____

_____

_____

_____

1.2 ‖ Anger Cycle

Certain things happen before you become angry. Usually, thought or event happens that triggers a certain mood in you. You then act on that mood (behavior).

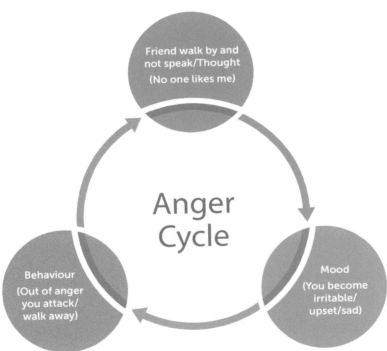

What is a Trigger?

A trigger is a reminder of past trauma. The reminder makes a person feel overwhelmed, sad, anxious, or panicky. A trigger is something that causes you to remember or relive a previous (past) experience or event.

General Points about Triggers:

- A trigger can be positive or negative.
- It is not uncommon to have triggers from things/areas that you are unaware that it is a trigger. This means that the trigger can happen out of the blue, and you have no idea why it happened, and sometimes you might not know when it happened.
- A memory can lie dormant for years, which means that something that can happen to a person when they are young (age 10) and they cannot remember it until they are well into their adulthood. A trigger is what brings the memory back to up.
- A trigger can be reoccurring and happen every time the same feeling/emotions occur.
- Positive triggers are not a problem, and we enjoy those. It is the negative triggers that cause us problems, and we often want to avoid it. So, let us go further into depth about negative triggers.
- Triggers occur in many forms and can occur with or without warning.
- Triggers can cause you to lose track of your thoughts, surroundings
- A trigger can be "relived" multiple times
- A trigger can be internal or external.

Three Types of Responses to Anger Triggers

1. **Emotional** - feelings we experience (example anger, fear, confusion)

2. **Cognitive Responses** - internal observations of our ideas and thoughts about the situation when we are angry. Our "inner voice."

3. **Physical Response** - responses in the body from heightened stress (increased perspiration, shallow or increased breathing, rapid heartbeat)

Since we are discussing anger, let us go over some triggers that can cause you to get angry.

Examples of things that could trigger you to have responded with anger:

- **Certain Surroundings or Environment**. Sometimes the physical location or situation that we find ourselves in can influence angry feelings. We do not often pay attention to background or environments that annoy us or create frustration. For example, being in crowded areas and people bumping into you could be a trigger for you. So now, every time you are in a crowd, you are easily annoyed and easily angered when people bump into you.

- **Personal Health.** When we are not feeling well (i.e., headache), it is common for us to have a "short temper." Other physical issues that can cause feelings of anger to include tired, pain, hunger, and depression. All these issues can contribute to angry responses from time to time.

- **Attitudes and expectations.** This is when we create our anger when we think of ways things are not going our way or the way we think they should go. Expecting people to be predictable, just, fair, and honest is not an unrealistic expectation. However, we do not have any control over how people react. There are also times when we expect our accomplishments to be recognized, and when they are not, feelings of anger can arise.

Other Factors that may cause anger:

- Rudeness, poor interpersonal skills, poor service from other people
- Tiredness (not getting enough sleep)
- Hunger
- Injustice (being bullied, humiliated, or embarrassed)
- Illness/Sickness/Disability
- Grief (loss of family, friend)
- Stress-related to family, health, work, money
- Unrealistic deadlines
- Things beyond our control (example-stuck in traffic)
- Physically or mentally unwell
- Pain
- Frustration-fail to reach a goal (ex. getting an "A" on a test)
- Fear (threats of violence, physical, or verbal abuse)
- Disappointment (expectations/desires are not met)
- Resentment (feeling hurt, rejected, or offended.)

Nine characteristics/traits that people may have that could increase or cause them to respond with anger:

This area is not to put labels on you or anyone else but to enlighten with the knowledge that individual characteristics/traits are associated with anger problems.

1. **Low Frustration/Tolerance** - the inability to tolerate things well, easily irritated, and having a "short fuse." Sometimes you may not say anything, sometimes you may explode, or you might resort to physical violence (hitting).

2. **Judgmental and Critical Reactions -**trouble recognizing the importance of other's needs, feelings, or opinions. This person strongly believes that they know the way things are and the way things should be and expect others to always agree with them.

3. **Perfectionism-** feel like nothing that you do or accomplish is "good enough." Sometimes you may put off actions/projects for the "right time." It can lead to feelings of mediocrity or worthlessness, which causes them to be angry. This type of anger is usually within.

4. **All or Nothing** - Dysfunctional thinking where you feel everything is either right or wrong. In real life, things are not always concrete. Instead of "all right or all wrong," there are different levels of agreements that maybe some right and some wrong. When you think of everything as all right or all wrong, this is what we call "black and white" thinking.

5. **Possessiveness** - This person displays a lack of trust, or they are insecure by trying to control everything around them. When they are unable to control things, they become angry.

6. **Poor Communication -**This person has trouble staying focused and listening carefully when the conversation is taking place, or they may feel like they have nothing to say, so they say nothing. However, they are angry afterward because they feel ignored and misunderstood.

7. **Punitive Behavior-** This person wants to punish people if they do not do things the "right way," which is defined by them (from things they have learned/believe).

8. **Addictive Personality-** feel like they need things. These things can be food, relationships, exercise, substances (drug/alcohol). They have impulsive behavior (doing things without thinking), which usually is done out of anger and gets them in trouble.

9. **Using Anger as Power-** They stay on the defensive and use anger to avoid

feeling vulnerable, small, or showing your true feelings. They take things people say to them as a personal insult.

Key Point: *Keep in mind that I am describing characteristics/traits that a person could have, which do not give an indication of who the person is. A characteristic can be changed.*

For the following situations, describe a trigger that you can identify from each of the following:

A family member_____

A friend_____

A Stranger_____

At School_____

At work _____

A sibling_____

A teacher_____

How Anger Affects our Body

Earlier, remember, I mention that anger is a healthy emotion. Well, anger is considered healthy because it is a part of our "fight or flight" response system within our body. When you are in a situation where there is a perceived or real threat, adrenalin is released into your bloodstream. This automatic response is that your body is energizing itself and preparing to either escape the situation or defend itself. There is nothing you have to do to start this process, and there is nothing you can do to stop this process. It just happens automatically.

When you get angry, some hormones are also naturally released, which causes our bodies to respond. Because of these hormones, physical and emotional responses naturally happen within our bodies as well. If the responses are negative and happen all the time untreated, unhealthy things will start to happen to our bodies physically and mentally.

Physical Response in our Bodies to Anger (Fight/Flight)

- Clenched fist
- Clenching of the jaw or grinding teeth
- Shallow breathing/or breathlessness
- Increased heart rate
- Perspiring, sweaty palms
- Trembling or shaking lips, hands
- Rocking motion while sitting
- Pacing
- Being rude
- Losing sense of humor
- Talking louder
- Increased cravings (sugar, chocolate.)

Expressions of Anger:

Verbal

- Cry
- Yell
- Scream
- Sarcasm
- Abusive language
- Talking disrespectfully to someone
- Talking non-stop.

Physically

- Clenched fist/teeth
- Glaring
- Eating
- Pouting/sulking
- Pacing back and forth

- Throwing things
- Fighting
- Withdrawal.

Internal and External Examples of Things that Causes Anger

- **Ill Humor** - When you take things too seriously and become moody/upset, which causes you to get angry easier.

- **Frustrations** - When you try to do something, and you cannot because it is blocked, or you become disappointed, thus possibly leading to angry feelings.

- **Tension** - When your stress level is high, and you are "on edge." This will possibly cause you to become angry easier.

- **Withdrawal/avoidance** - When you avoid conflict and walk away without resolving the issue. You internalize (hold it in), and this causes you to easily Anger.

Key Point: *It is not people or events that make your Anger. It is the way you react to people or events that makes you angry.*

As hard as it is to believe, sometimes, there are healthy, effective ways to manage Anger without going into a rage and becoming physically or emotionally violent.

You should control your anger and not let your anger control you. We all respond to Anger in different ways because of our life experiences, personal beliefs, and world views.

WHAT'S ON YOUR MIND?

_____

_____

_____

_____

_____

What are some external/outside (people/events) triggers that you have/can identify?

What are some internal/personal (memories, worries/angry thoughts) triggers that you have/can identify?

Describe a time when just thinking about things in the past has made you angry.

Why do we get Angry?

Anger comes from an internal response to things in your environment that happen based on how you feel about these things. Anger is often learned behavior and repeated from what we have seen in our homes, and the way our family/friends respond to things that make them angry. The response can come from something internal or external. Sometimes, you will have very little control over the external factors, but you do have "complete" control of your internal control and how you think about, interpret, and respond to things.

In life, many things irritate or annoy us. When these feelings or emotions become too strong, then we often move into an angry mode where our thoughts are negative and ineffective. The way we respond to Anger is from learned behaviors (what we have seen or experienced). Since how we respond to Anger is learned, that means we can unlearn the bad behaviors and learn new responses to Anger. But to change, you must want to.

Emotional Response to Anger

- Sad
- Guilty
- Resentful
- Depressed
- Irritation
- Desire to "run away" from situations
- Anxiety
- Feeling/desire to lash out (verbally/ physically.)

Physical Health Problems that can Occur with Because of Long Term Unresolved Anger:

- High blood pressure/Heart Disease
- Sleep problems
- Stomach problems (indigestion)
- Skin disorders
- Impaired immune system
- Aches and pains, usually HA
- Weakened immune system.

Psychological (Mental) Problems that Can Occur from Unresolved Anger:

- Decreased Self-Confidence
- Eating disorders
- Depression
- Alcohol/Drug use
- Self-injury
- Thoughts of self-harm (suicidal)
- Anxiety
- Helpless/Hopeless.

All the previous things mentioned that unresolved Anger could cause is why it is so important that you learn now how to deal with Anger. Because, as you can see, it does not just go away. The habits you develop now will stay with you into your adulthood.

Which of these anger responses can you identify?

These physical responses are some cues that you should recognize that you may be getting angry. It is important to recognize these clues early to decrease the physical symptoms of Anger, which would allow you to have more control over the Anger itself.

Three Ways of Dealing with Anger

1. **Stuffing-** "swallowing" your Anger or only not allowing yourself to experience Anger. Ignoring it.

2. **Escalating-** You let the Anger out, not hold it in. You let it out on whoever is around you at that exact moment of release.

3. **Managing-** You express your anger in a socially appropriate and healthy way, by practicing/having self-control.

Section 2

Anger Management

"The best fighter is never angry"

Lau Tsu

2.1 What is Anger Management?

Anger Management is a process where you are open, honest, direct, and moves in a positive direction of what to do in situations that cause you anger.

The focus is on a specific behavior that triggers an angry response from you and in the present (here and now).

Anger management is like any other skill, it takes practice, and you must recognize it, admit it, and learn your triggers. Creating a log can help you identify the areas you have mastered and the areas you need to work on. Start with making clear statements about the situation that made you angry. Every skill must have work and practice for anyone to get good at that skill. You might want to practice with a neutral person by doing role-playing. You will not only get practice but will be able to get feedback on how you are doing.

Things You Can do When You Recognize You are Becoming Angry?

This is common what I hear when I discuss not being angry or not letting anger control you. I hear, "Well, what do I do then"? That's a valid and good question because unless you do something different, you will continue to repeat the same negative behaviors when you become angry that could lead to increasing problems as the anger returns over and over.

Learning to recognize and express anger appropriately can make a big difference in your life.

Anger Can Help You:

- ⮑ **Reach goals**- Trying to reach goals can be frustrating. Frustration can lead to anger, which in turn could motivate you to work harder.
- ⮑ **Communicate with others-** talking about your Anger can keep it from building up. When you are not angry, you will enjoy communication with family/friends better. It is also more comfortable for you to communicate.
- ⮑ **Solve problems**- Anger is a sign that alerts you that something is wrong. It may serve as a warning for you, so you need to think about attention to your feelings and attitudes.
- ⮑ **Handle emergencies and protect yourself**- Anger can cause an instant burst of strength and energy. Maybe a natural response that allows you to react very quickly if you are in danger.
- ⮑ **Stay healthy**- long term unresolved anger can lead to mental/physical problems.
- ⮑ **Feel better about yourself**- using calm effective coping skills can help you stay in control of a situation that would be negative or end if you lose control and "blow up."

Anger Can Work Against You:

- ⮑ **Verbal attacks or physical assault**- you may lose control and attack others physically or verbally. For example, you may throw or break things, yell, insult, or threaten, slap, shove, kick, or hit.
- ⮑ **Other criminal behavior**- Anger is often a driving force behind criminal behavior such as destruction of property, murder, other violent crimes.
- ⮑ **Substance abuse**- drugs and alcohol are commonly used to mask things, and Anger is one of the common emotions that people start to use substances to hide their feelings/pain/things they are going through.

Have you ever experienced anger? If so explain.

2.2 Tips That You Can Use When Dealing With Someone Else's Anger

The ability to feel Anger is something we are all born with. The right to feel Anger is personal, and we are all entitled to our angry feelings. How we express Anger is another issue. We are not entitled to choose how someone responds to Anger, but we are responsible for the way we respond. If we act negatively just because someone else acts negatively, we are still responsible for the things we do. We also must face the consequences of how we do or do not handle our Anger.

Helpful Ways to respond when responding to someone angry

Expressing anger negatively can destroy relationships, job performance, and for most of you, performance in school. Since we have some responsibility for building and maintaining good relationships, it is important to know how to act when we are in a situation with an angry person.

Tips How to Respond to an Angry Person:

- Keep your cool! (easier said than done sometimes but very important)
- Do not respond with anger. Always remember that anger can lead people to say things they do not mean. Criticism, threats, or name-calling will not help resolve anger situations either.
- Do not take it personally. As hard as it is, try to understand why the person is angry. His or her feeling may have little or nothing to do with you.
- Listen to the person. Sometimes an angry person just needs to "blow off steam." Let them get it off their chest without interrupting. Maintain eye contact to show that you are listening.
- Think of solutions together. If you have a conflict with someone, try to find a solution that you both can agree on. But you will only be able to do this if both of you are calm.
- Do not take chances. If you are worried about your safety or theirs, get help right away.
- Meditation use to help calm you and clear your mind.
- Take a time out or cool off period if things are too heated. This will allow the person to calm down and revisit the conversation when things are calmer.

How Can You Manage Your Anger?

Managing your anger means that you learn to use coping skills to work through problems, relax, make a better decision, and get help if you need it. Remember, it will happen.

Describe a time when you had to managed your anger?

Anger-reducing Techniques to Use When Things Start to Make You Angry, and You Need to Calm Down

Deep Breathing

- Sit comfortably or lie on your back
- Breathe in slowly and deeply for a count of five
- Hold your breath for a count of five
- Breathe out slowly for a count of five, pushing out all the air
- Repeat until you feel calm and relaxed

Have a Sense of Humor?

- First, this does not work for everyone. But sometimes having a good sense of humor can help some people avoid getting angry. Finding humor in minor troubles can help to decrease feelings of annoyance and keep Anger from setting in.

Get a Hobby

- A hobby can provide a productive outlet for tension and energy as it takes your mind away from thinking of the negative situation. Some people like to listen to music, read, write, or draw, and color. When you choose a hobby, just make sure it is something that you like to do.

Journaling

- Writing about your thoughts and feelings calmly and at your own pace. You can even write a letter and tear it up once the letter is written (you do not have to mail it or give it to anyone.)

Pleasant Imagery/Visualization

This is when you use your imagination to help you relax, which decreases your Anger.

- Step 1: Sit in a comfortable chair or lie down.
- Step 2: Imagine a pleasant, peaceful scene (example beach) and picture yourself in the setting.
- Step 3: Focus on the scene and continue to focus until you feel refreshed and relaxed.

Meditation

- Wear loose, comfortable clothing
- Find a quiet place
- Sit or lie down
- Close your eyes
- Take slow deep breaths
- Concentrate on a single word, object, or calming thought
- If thoughts or images enter your mind, do not worry, or focus on that, relax, and return to what you were focusing on
- Continue until you feel relaxed and refreshed.

Muscle relaxation

When you are angry, your muscles become tense. Doing progressive muscle relaxation exercises can help relieve this tension.

- Step 1: Wear loose, comfortable clothing. Sit in a comfortable chair or lie down.
- Step 2: Tense the muscles in areas such as your face, back of neck, or shoulders for about 5-10 seconds. Then relax for 20 seconds. You can use this with any muscle groups in your body.

Rest

The amount of sleep everyone needs varies from person to person but usually is between 6-9 hours. Anger can make it difficult for you to sleep, especially falling asleep. When you do not get enough sleep that your body requires, you may be irritable, which can increase your Anger.

Some helpful tips for falling asleep:

- Go to bed at the same time each night
- Wake up at the same time
- Turn all electronics off (which I know is hard). Do not sleep with the tv on.
- Avoid drinks that contain caffeine 3-4 hours before time to go to bed.

Physical Activity

- Physical activity is a way to quickly and safely let out strong feelings, and if done regularly, could improve your overall health. Walking, swimming, tennis, dancing, yoga, and running are all some examples of physical actives that you can do. You might not want to hear this, but chores such as cleaning your room can be an effective outlet for Anger. Do not overdo it if you decide to do physical activity. Warm-up and cool down, so you do not injure yourself.

Counting

- Counting is a way to give you time to calm down, focus, and think clearly. Commonly we say count to 10, but you pick the number that works for you, it might be 20, 30, or even 100. Sometimes people will choose to count backward because this requires more effort and thought to implement.

Talk Rather Than Act Out Your Angry Emotions

- When your Anger is triggered, it is best to talk to someone you trust that is not involved with your rage."Venting" or talking with someone neutral can help you get a different perspective on things. Do not vent to someone who will encourage you to be angry. You want to vent to someone that will help you positively resolve things. Sometimes others will give you input that will help create solutions to an angry situation that you may not have thought of on your own.

Explore Your Options.

○ It is not uncommon that when we are angry, we feel stuck. This is when we only look at "concrete" solutions and not anything in-between. Sometimes it is helpful to give yourself some days to cool off and think of different scenarios. Time may help you think of different perspectives that you had not thought of because of your Anger.

Recall What Solutions That Worked for You in the Past

○ Recalling things that worked in the past is often a reminder that things have worked out for you before and that your current situation is temporary. No matter how mad/uncomfortable your feelings are, they will go away. Acting impulsively, exploding, or sulking will only make things worse. This is not an excuse to ignore the Anger and hope it will go away. It is a reminder that you have dealt with Anger before in an effective way, and you can do it again.

Reward Yourself

○ When you successfully handle an awkward situation, be proud, and reward yourself. When you allow yourself to feel proud that you handled your Anger well, it will help you remember that you can do it again in the future.

> Describe a situation that you acted out of anger, and, after the fact, or now, you realized you could have handled things differently.

> Which Anger techniques have you used in the past to deal with Anger?

Which techniques have you not used, but will practice and use now?

Ways to Assess if the Anger Coping Skills You are Using are Effective

Evaluate: How did you do?

- An important process of changing any behavior is to reflect and review how well you are doing.
- You need to know if it's working and if you can continue with the coping skill or if you need to make changes to what you are doing.

Self-coaching

- This is when you identify how your Anger coping skills are going.
- If you feel you did not' handle your Anger well, or as well as you could have, it's important to identify the areas that you need to make changes.

Self-reward

- When you do well, acknowledge it and reward yourself. You must reward yourself. The reward does not have to be something big; it can be something as small as telling yourself you did well and having ice cream.

When You Get Angry, Ask Yourself

- Are my level of Anger and my reaction out of proportion to the trigger?

Sometimes there are hidden underlying things in our mind that cause us to be angry or overreact to minor annoyances with an angry outburst that exceeds the expected response to the situation. It is often referred to as "blowing up."

- Am I directing my Anger at an innocent person?

Assess if you are angry with the person who triggered your feelings. For example, your mom makes you mad, and then you go to school and end up getting into trouble with the teacher because you were rude when she asked you a simple question.

⊃ Am I taking things personally?

When you take things personally, it can lead you to become angry when the way you take things might not be the real situation.

⊃ Is this how I usually respond in similar situations?

Sometimes we respond to situations the same way because "It's what you have always done," which does not make it right. Your response could be a learned negative behavior that needs to change.

⊃ Am I trying to take charge of my Anger?

Anger is collective when one feels that they are losing control. The best way to show control is when you control your feelings and react in a calm effective manner.

Make Clear Statements:

I am angry because _____

_____

What triggered my anger? _____

_____

My response _____

_____

Something I did well in this situation _____

_____

Something I could have done better _____

_____

Anger Log

An **Anger log** is a tool for helping you become aware of your angry feelings and responses. It is suitable for self-observation, and a way to monitor your progress.

Anger Management Log

Trigger to Anger	My Response	Something I did well	Something I could have done better	Date

Now that you have learned more about Anger and how to recognize Anger, another helpful skill you might want to use is how to develop an anger management plan to develop effective coping skills.

Steps of Developing an Anger Management Plan.

1. Set Positive Goals and a Time Frame

⮑ Your goals should address a specific behavior and your reaction. For example, your goal could be to communicate your feelings using an "I" statement whenever you get angry. You can set more than one goal for yourself, but do not try and meet too many at one time. If you try to accomplish too many things at the same time, it is less likely that you will reach any of them.

2. Get Support

⮑ Tell someone that you trust about your goals so that they can offer some support, encouragement, and advice. You should use your support team if you are having trouble with any anger issues. It is also ok if you need to seek professional help such as a school counselor, therapist, or mental health professional.

3. Track Your Progress

⮑ A daily log or journal will help you track your process. Seeing improvement over time can help keep you from feeling discouraged.

4. Reward Yourself!

⮑ Treat yourself when you reach a goal or get halfway there. For example, go to a movie or enjoy a special meal.

TAKING ACTION
Anger Management Plan

Keep track of your anger over the next couple of days.

Goal	My action plan	Target date	Reward

Who can help you?

1._____

2._____

3._____

4._____

5._____

6._____

7._____

8._____

9._____

10._____

11.._____

12._____

13._____

14.._____

15.._____

Goal box should answer the question: What do I want to change about how I handle my Anger?What would I like to be doing differently when I am Angry?

2.3 Steps You Can Use to Get Back in Control When You Get Angry, or You are in an Angry Situation with Someone Else

Start by Taking a "Timeout"

Stop what you are doing. This is the hardest thing to do, but it is the best thing you can do when you get angry. This needs to happen when you first start to feel your anger warning signs developing, and you start thinking angry thoughts. Tell yourself to stop. This gives you a minute to help calm down and think clearly before you react.

Try to Relax

- Count to 10 or 100 if it is terrible
- Get a drink of water
- Take a walk
- Take several slow, deep breaths.

Leave, If Necessary

If you are angry with another person and they are in front of you, tell them that you need to take a time out. Go for a walk or a safe place to calm down. However, avoid driving.

Return When You are Calm

Once you have gotten your Anger under control, go back and talk with the person or face the situation that triggered your Anger. You do not want the anger issues to go unresolved because the Anger could grow and turn into rage or cause you mental/health problems. After all, you have internalized the Anger.

Remember to Calm Down

- Think carefully before you speak. This will help decrease your chances of saying something you will be sorry for later.

Name the Problem

- In a calm and clear manner, explain why you are angry or what the problem is. Do not use insults or make threats. If you come across as defensive, upset people will be less likely to listen to you or consider your point.

Use "I" Statements

- After describing the problem, use "I" statements to tell the person how you feel. "I" statements help you to focus on you, your needs, wants, and feelings. This will also help the listener avoid feeling responsible or criticized.

Identify Solutions

- Be specific about what you would like to change or see happen in the future to make the situation better. It is wise that if you have a conflict with another person, that you try to find the solution together.

Get Help if You Need it

- Talk to a family member or friend that you trust. Having someone to express your anger in a constructive manner can help if you need to talk to a counselor, therapist, or other mental health professional. This could be a great way to learn to express your feelings (i.e., role-playing).

Key Points:

Do not hold a grudge.
After a disagreement, be willing to forgive.
Asking for help is a sign of strength, not weakness.

Avoid Negative Reactions Such As:

Refusing to Let Go

Sometimes, it is hard to get past your Anger because painful events tend to stay with us for a long time, especially if they are not resolved. Sometimes, it hard to let go of a painful event, but know that if you do not, they just continue to grow. Then you run the risk of becoming obsessed with angry thoughts and may develop thoughts or hopes of getting revenge.

Bottle Things Up

This is when you do not let your feelings out. People think this is helpful, but it is not and often making you feel worse. What happens is over time, the feelings build and build, and when they come out, it could be in the form of an angry outburst. Sometimes these outbursts are projected on those you are not even angry with. Remember, angry feelings also contribute to the health and physical problems.

Blaming

Blame does not solve problems. It is important to learn to take responsibility for your feeling and actions. This includes the negative, as well as positive actions.

Using Alcohol or Drugs

Using alcohol and drugs to dull Anger does not work. Using substances may mask angry feelings, but this is a temporary fix that can cause you longer problems in the long run. This often brings the opposite results as they can cause you to become angrier and have difficulty focusing or thinking clearly.

Key Point: You can take steps to change how you react to Anger.

Section 3

Bullying

"You should never make fun of something that a person can't change about themselves."

Phil Lester

3.1 What is Bullying?

Bullying is repeated aggressive behaviors, actions, or threats done to someone or a group of people to cause harm, fear, distress,or pain in a persistent way that produces an imbalance of power (one person overrides another one in some form or fashin). Bullying can be verbal, physical, emotional or psychological, or through social media outlets.

Bullying is a topic that is being talked about worldwide because of the increase in bullying at school and online. It is a sensitive subject of the hurt, shame, and guilt associated with being bullied. Some poeple also don't understand what makes a situation "bullying," so it's ignored, mislabeled, or things are said and done to make the victim feel shameful, or as if it's their fault. Victims are often told, "Don't be a cry baby," "Man up'" or "Stop being a tattletale."

As a Psychiatric Mental Health Nurse Practitioner (PMHNP), I see children and adults with problems associated with Bullying and other mental health issues. When I talk to children, one of the everyday things I hear is, "I wasn't bulling, I was just playing."

If you do things intentionally to cause another person harm, shame, fear, etc.... it is a form of bullying. No one wants to be made a mockery, and they do not see it as funny. It is hurtful and often shameful to the person that is being bullied.

So, what makes it "bullying" versus "playing?

Bullying is a "learned behavior" that often starts at an early age. Have you seen toddlers not wanting to share saying "mine"? I am not saying that's bullying, but what happens if that child is not taught to share? They grow up with the same constant mindset and behavior that could escalate to different degrees and intensity. This can create an environment where it teaches children to have control over or dominate others. They are not being taught to consider the feelings of others. This also creates an environment where hostility and aggression can be taught/learned. Have you ever seen a toddler take their toy back from someone? They usually snatch it. This same environment may also be teaching the other toddler to be sensitive, overly cautious with others, and to have feelings of anxiety.

How would you define Bullying? Describe using some specific actions.

Have you ever been bullied? Describe the situation.

How did it make you feel? Did anyone help you?

What was the outcome? Or is it still on-going?

Have you told someone? If so, who? And was it helpful? If you have not told anyone, why not?

Have you ever bullied someone? Describe the situation, and what was the outcome?

How did that make you feel?

Adolescent years can be when kids feel like it is ok to be mean to one another. However, Bullying is not just "kids being kids." Bullying is intentional and repeated. Bullying is not a random act, and it is frequent.

Dr. Dan Olweus's definition of Bullying is widely used and accepted.

"Bullying...is a pattern of repeated aggressive behavior with negative intent, directed from one person to another where there is a power imbalance."

Olweus has identified **three critical conditions** that can be used to determine Bullying from other forms of aggressive behavior. The three conditions are Power, Frequency, and Intent to Harm.

Power - some people bully for a sense of power, authority, or individual status among peers and often try and get others to go along with it.

Frequency - as stated earlier, Bullying is done over and over. The person being bullied becomes fearful when the Bullying begins to happen. The anticipation is something that can have long term detrimental and debilitating effects. There is not a certain number of times that it must happen to cause permanent and lasting effects. Sometimes something can be done one time and be traumatic for a person the same way it would if it happened ten times.

Intent to Harm - the bully has specific intent to harm verbally, physically, emotionally. Some think that if it is not physically done (hitting) that it is not hurtful, but that is not true.

Sometimes Bullying may start in playful ways (pranks, jokes, roughhousing) and then develop into Bullying as one person realizes the "power" he/she may gain. "Joking around" can be hurtful and should be avoided. It is not appropriate to hurt someone, even when you are joking.

Bullying can be directly or indirectly done.

Direct Bullying is when the Bullying is done face-to-face between the bully and the victim.

Indirect Bullying is when the bully attacks the victim›s social standing or reputation (spreading rumors, writing notes, etc.)

Facts about Bullying

- It is a learned behavior
- Conscious, willful, and deliberate
- Repeated over time by the same person (group)
- Intended to harm, induce fear (intentional)
- Threat of aggression
- Create terror
- Imbalance of power
- Not about anger
- Excuse making the bully feel good by putting someone else down
- Has long-term effects (depression, suicidal ideation)
- Form a sense of entitlement
- Intolerance of differences
- At liberty to exclude (reject/ignore.)

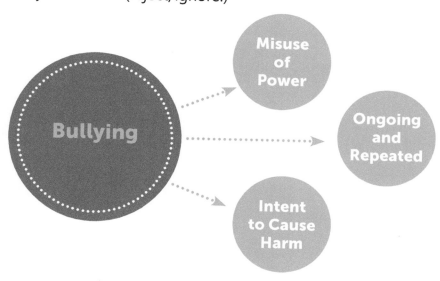

Teasing vs. Bullying

Teasing

⊃ When someone makes fun of someone in a humored way, it is not serious, and the person being made fun of can/will laugh about it.

⊃ It is usually done by someone who cares about the person (family/friend).

⊃ If you get a bit upset about a tease, it is not a strong feeling and will soon go away on its own.

⊃ Everyone has a turn. Everyone teases each other, and no one person is being picked on alone.

⊃ If teasing is hurtful, it is usually by mistake, and the person will stop and apologize.

⊃ Laughter "within."

Bullying

⊃ It is cruel

⊃ It is meant to hurt

⊃ When it singles someone out or is one-sided (the same person is being picked on), or the same person is doing the Bullying)

⊃ An imbalance of power is created. The bully often wants power by hurting others, taking things, or making them do things they do not want to do

⊃ Laughter "at."

3.2 | Types of Bullying?

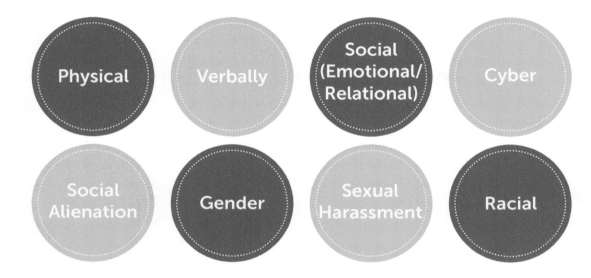

Physical

Verbally

Social (Emotional/Relational)

Cyber

Social Alienation

Gender

Sexual Harassment

Racial

Have you ever experienced Bullying? If so, what type of Bullying and how did you respond? Have you ever been the bully towards someone else? If so, what did you do? Answer all that applies to you. Be honest.

Physical Bullying

Physical Bullying is when someone uses physical action to hurt and gain power or control over another person. Some common examples of physical Bullying are:

➲ Pushing

➲ Kicking

➲ Hitting

➲ Spitting

➲ Shoving

➲ Threatening with a weapon

➲ Destruction of personal property

➲ Stealing.

Physical Bullying is the most visible type of Bullying. The bully is often bigger, stronger, and more aggressive than their peers.

> Have you experienced physical Bullying? If so, what happened, and what was the outcome?

Verbal Bullying

Verbal bullying is the act of saying or writing words that are mean or hurtful. Verbal bullying is powerful as the words can turn into a deeper wound in the long-term than those of physical bullying and leave long-lasting emotional scaring. The hurtful words become "normalized" over time that the person starts to believe they are right, and this is what causes the damage. For example, if a person is told they are ugly overtime for many years, despite how they genuinely look, they will always feel ugly.

Verbal bullying may also be harder to prove because verbal bullying does not leave evidence. Most of the time, it is one person's word against the other person. If there are not any witnesses around, this may be difficult to prove who is telling the truth.

Some examples of verbal Bullying include:

- Name-calling
- Teasing
- Mocking
- Intimidating telephone calls or voicemails
- Racist, sexist, or homophobic remarks

- Verbal threats against property
- Verbal threats of bodily harm
- Coercion
- Extortion.

Have you experienced verbal Bullying? If so, what happened, and what was the outcome? Have you ever verbally bullied someone? If so, what was the outcome?

Emotional Bullying

This type of bullying is anything that causes emotional pain. For example, a person that is told that they are stupid throughout numerous years will start to believe that. As a result, this affects their self-esteem and belief in themselves, which tends to make them have difficulty making and achieving goals.

Have you ever had someone say to you if you are my friend, you will? Or if you love me.? These types of questions, or rather, these types of demands, are examples of emotional bullying. It is directly tied to a certain feeling such as love, wanting to be accepted, fear of being alone, or fear of rejection.

Examples of Emotional Bullying

- Destroying and manipulating relationships

- Embarrassment and humiliation

- Negative body language (facial expressions, turning your back to someone)

- Threatening gestures

- Hurtful graffiti

- Mean notes passed around or sent to someone.

This type of bullying is indirectly tied to verbal bullying. Emotional bullying is subtle and often occurs more with girls than boys.

Cyber Bullying

Cyberbullying is where the attack is made via digital space, electrotonic means, or of information and communication technologies, such as email, cellphone, and text messages, instant messages, defamatory personal web sites, or defamatory online personal polling web sites to support deliberate, repeated, and hostile behavior by an individual or group that is intended to harm others.

Key Point: *Cyberbullying is not as harmless as it may seem. Sometimes because the person being bullied cannot be seen, the effects do not "seem" as bad.*

Research has shown that cyberbullying can potentially be worse than any of the other types of bullying, and I wholeheartedly agree. This is because of the number of people that can see the comments or negative things posted. Instead of 10 people, it can turn into 10,000 or more very quickly if the posts go viral. It is sad to say that most of the negative things go viral, and people all over the world can see social media posts.

Examples of Cyberbullying:

- Creating a blog/website/poll about a person to humiliate or harass them
- Post rude, mean, or insulting comments about someone via chat
- Sending viruses, spyware, or hacking programs to someone to spy or control his or her computer remotely
- Use information shared in confidence and making it public.

I cannot count the number of times I have gotten a text message with a "snapshot" of something another person sent to them.

Another thing that makes cyberbullying bad is that sometimes it is difficult to prove. People go out of their way to create false accounts and false social media pages to harm others while they hide in secrecy and pretend it is "not me." With the creation of false pages, unless the police get involved, it is hard to figure out the owners of the false accounts.

Sometimes people get caught up in doing things for "likes" or comments on social media and not realize that it is a form of bullying.

Have you ever experienced Cyberbullying? If so, what was the outcome?

Social Alienation

Social alienation is when things such as gossiping or spreading rumors about others are done to exclude someone from a group or to encourage others to exclude people. Social alienation is also a way to cause embarrassment to others.

Everyone wants to be in the "in-crowd," especially during the teen years. So, what happens when someone goes out of their way to make someone feel left out, to make others not want to talk to them. It's called social alienation. This usually happens during lunchtime or recess. Social alienation is when things such as gossiping or spreading rumors about others are done to exclude someone from a group or to encourage others to exclude people. Social alienation is also a way to cause embarrassment to others, so no one wants to be around them.

Examples of Social Alienation Bullying

⮑ Not letting certain people sit at lunch tables

⮑ Only picking certain people to be on their sides for sports

⮑ Social exclusions (only being friends with certain types of people.)

Have you ever been socially alienated from a group? Have you ever socially alienated anyone from your group? How did this make you feel? What was the outcome?

Gender Bullying

Gender Bullying is the identity that describes how someone feels, appears, or acts.

Disclaimer: *The purpose of this section is not to agree or disagree with anything, nor will it apply to any religious beliefs or my opinion. I just want to make sure you understand what gender bullying is.*

Example of Gender Bullying:

➲ "I feel like a boy even though I was born a female." Which is "sex." Sex is a person's biological status as a male or female.

Today, gender bullying has increased because there are more laws and acceptance that a person has the right to choose what gender they are. These laws are applied to children as well as adults. Gender bullying is not harassment, but it is right above harassment. If you are not careful, you could easily cross the line.

However, gender bullying occurs when society's expectation of what an individual gender should differ from what the individual decides or prefers to identify with.

For example, a female identifying as male because that is how she has felt all her life now dresses as a male and requests to be called by a different name, Sam, instead of Samantha. Some members of society do not agree or accept her preference as a male and refuse to call her Sam.

This can lead us to gender stereotypes.

A gender stereotype is a "fixed" idea about the way a girl or boy is "supposed to dress or appear." This stereotype can refer to sex, or it could refer to things such as "girls can't play football."

 A person is entitled to how they feel, but it is not appropriate to call someone names or do inappropriate things to a person just because you do not agree with their personal "gender preference." If someone does mean or inappropriate things to someone because of their gender preference, then it is considered gender bullying.

Have you ever been bullied because of gender preference? Have you ever been bullied anyone because of gender preference? Have you seen someone bullied because of their gender preference? What was the outcome(s)?

Sexual Bullying

Sexual bullying is when a person makes uncomfortable comments, advances, gestures in a sexual orientation towards another person, which can be done with comments, videos, physical, or gestures.

Sexual bullying can be a difficult subject to discuss and even harder to report. Why? Because people have different definitions and opinions of flirting. Some things are accepted as flirting by some, and some things are not. The acceptance level is wide and varies.

Sexual Bullying can also depend on the person making the comments and gestures. The difference in the relationship or lack thereof can determine if the person finds the comments inappropriate.

Things that affect the interpretation of comments and gestures:

- Friend or stranger
- Age
- If the act is done in public or private
- Location
- The tone of the person's voice
- How the person looks at you
- The people around listening/looking
- How the act is done.

Everyone does not share the same point of view or interpretation of words that cause sexual offenses.

However, if you make a person uncomfortable or shameful, STOP the actions and comments immediately. If you know that they are painful, and you keep doing the same thing over and over, it can and may be considered Sexual bullying.

Do not get mad and say things like "you're weak" or "you can't take a joke," just stop. Sexual Bullying is severe, and it can lead to sexual harassment (which is against the law).

As a result, you could be fired from a job or sued, so it is best to form good habits now in your teen years, so it does not cost you later.

Examples of Sexual Bullying include:

- Sexual name-calling (baby, sugar, hot mama)
- Crude comments (your butt is so big)
- Vulgar gestures
- Uninvited touching
- Sexual propositioning.

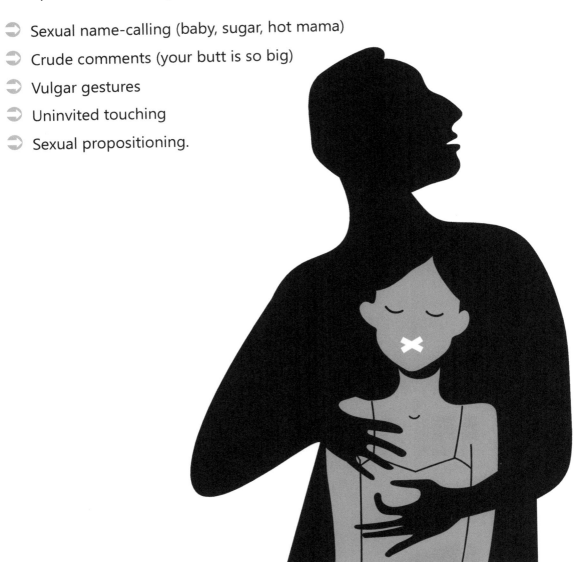

Key Point: *Sexual Bullying occurs more often with girls than boys. Sexting can also lead to sexual Bullying. For example, a girl might send her boyfriend a photo of herself, and the boyfriend shares it with everyone when they break up. The girl then becomes a victim because her peers may call her names (slut or tramp) or make fun of her appearance. They may also make insulting comments about her. Some boys might see this as an open invitation for them to proposition her sexually.*

Have you ever been in a situation where sexual Bullying has occurred? If so, what was the outcome? How did that make you feel?

Have you ever been accused of sexually bullying someone? If so, what was the outcome? How did that make you feel? Have you ever witnessed someone else being sexually bullied? What was the result? How did that make you feel?

Prejudice Bullying

Prejudicial Bullying is based on dislikes towards people because of race, religion, or sexual orientation.

This type of Bullying is when kids are targeted because of a difference between them and the person doing the Bullying. The bully singles this difference out.

Remember what makes a bully a "bully" is the repetition of "unwanted behavior." Prejudicial Bullying is generally from a thought (a stereotype that leads to a feeling of prejudice that causes discriminate actions against the same "type" of people repeatedly.)

The areas associated with prejudice bullying are self-explanatory so that I will not go into detail. This type of bullying is dangerous as it could lead to hate crimes, which is a serious offense.

Examples of Prejudicial Bullying:

- Race
- Religion
- Sexual Orientation
- Disability.

Have you ever experienced any type of prejudice bullying? Have you witnessed prejudice bullying? If so, what was the outcome?

Have you ever experienced any type of bullying? If so, what type(s) of bullying, and how did you respond?

Thought (Stereotype) → Feeling (Prejudice) → Action (Discriminate)

3.3 The Effects of Bullying

Bullying can affect every area of our body. These effects can last a lifetime if they are not dealt with.

Physical Health

Headache

Eating disorders (stomachaches, increased/decreased appetite)

Insomnia (unable to sleep)

Addictions (alcohol/drugs)

Depression

Anxiety

Suicidal.

Emotional Health

Sad

Anxiety

Depression

Anger

Decreased self-esteem

Isolation from others.

Academics

A cynical view of a school

Poor grades (low test scores)

Missing days of school increases

Truancy

Increase drop out risk

Grades improve because books/ studies are a way of "escape."

Violence

Become involved with criminal activities

Inward (suicide)

Outward (homicide.)

3.4 Six Different Types of Bullies

1 **THE CONFIDENT BULLY**

- Large ego
- Sense of superiority
- Sense of entitlement.

2 **THE SOCIAL BULLY**

- Uses taunts, rumors, gossip, and shunning
- Jealous of the positive qualities of others
- Hides their poor sense of self-esteem.

3 **THE SUFFICIENTLY STRENGTHENED (ARMORED) BULLY**

- Cool and detached
- Vicious and vindictive to victims
- Charming and deceptive in front of others
- Has a "flat affect."

So, what is a fully armored bully? This type of bully has a cold and emotionless exterior because their feels are so deeply buried that even they cannot identify them. They often have a cold and emotionless exterior because their feelings are so deeply buried that even they cannot identify them.

4 THE HYPERACTIVE BULLY

- ➲ Struggles with academics
- ➲ Does not process social skills accurately
- ➲ Has trouble making friends
- ➲ "He hit me first!"

5 THE BULLIED BULLY

- ➲ Bullied by adults or older kids
- ➲ Strikes out viciously at those who hurt them
- ➲ Strikes out viciously to those who are smaller/weaker
- ➲ Least popular of bully types.

6 THE BUNCH/GANG OF BULLIES

- ➲ The collective group of friends who want to make one person the scapegoat or exclude one person
- ➲ Usually perceived as "nice kids."
- ➲ Tries to control/dominate others
- ➲ Lack of empathy/remorse.

Bully's Reaction When Caught:

What happens when the bully gets caught?

When a bully gets caught, they tend to react in the following ways:

- Denial
- Trivialize the event (make it seem like it was not a big deal)
- Claim they are the victim by crying or accusing the other person of starting the incident.

The Victim

The "*victim*" is the person being bullied. There have been studies on what makes a victim vulnerable to bullying, and some of the common reasons why individual "victims" are targeted.

- Age (younger children are picked sometimes picked on by older children)
- Race
- How they look (fat, skinny, short, tall)
- Religion
- Academic ability (honor roll student vs. student struggling

- Children in special education classes
- Way they dress
- Early or late sexual development
- How much money they (family) have?
- Disabilities
- Factors related to parents (obese, handicapped, type of job parent has)
- Color of skin- not in a racial sense but within the same race (in AA -African Americans) as AA has many shades. Some children get teased about being "light-skinned" and some about being "dark-skinned."

The victim may also isolate from family and friends to hide. Bullying may cause them to be sad so that they will stay off to themselves, so no one will ask what is wrong. Anger is another emotion the victim might display in the form of outbursts, especially if they have younger siblings or pets in the home.

So, instead of developing healthy social skills, survival skills and strategies are being developed instead. Why? Because survival strategies are what the "victim" is now thinking about. They are thinking of ways they can avoid being bullied. The victim is thinking of ways they can get back at the bully without being hurt, without being caught, or how to get out of going to school.

The survival thinking affects how much energy the "victim" has left for focus and attention at school, interpersonal relationships (friends/family), ability to do homework, study for tests, work, etc. The reason why the grades of someone being bullied often drops, or they drop out of school altogether.

It is not uncommon for the victim not to tell anyone they are being bullied. I have heard many times; "why don't they understand?"

Some reasons why victims usually do not tell they are being bullied:

- Ashamed of being bullied
- Afraid of retaliation
- Do not think anyone will help
- Do not think anyone can help
- Been told, "bullying is an apart of growing up"
- Do not want to be labeled a "snitch"
- Bullied at home so they may believe Bullying is "ok" or "normal."

Key Point: *It does not matter what the reason is, Bullying is never ok, and it is never the "victim's" fault.*

Some warning signs of someone who might be being bullied:

- Abrupt disinterest in school
- Refuses to go to school
- Takes an unusual route to school
- Grades drop
- Poor concentration overall (school/home/community)
- Withdraws from family or friends (does not talk to anyone anymore when there was a relationship before)

- Isolates (stays in the room)

- Regularly claims to have lost lunch money or not hungry at school
- Steals from patents
- Sad, scared after received phone calls/emails
- Does things out of character
- Uses demeaning or derogatory language when speaking of peers
- Has disheveled, torn or missing clothing
- Have physical injuries not consistent with an explanation
- Has frequent headaches, stomachaches
- Difficulty sleeping.

Have you been a victim of Bullying? Did you tell anyone? Why or Why not?

Have you known someone that was a victim of Bullying? How did that make you feel?

The Bystander

The bystander is someone who witnesses the act of Bullying or event but does not participate in it.

Now some people feel there is nothing wrong with this because they think, "I didn't do nothing."

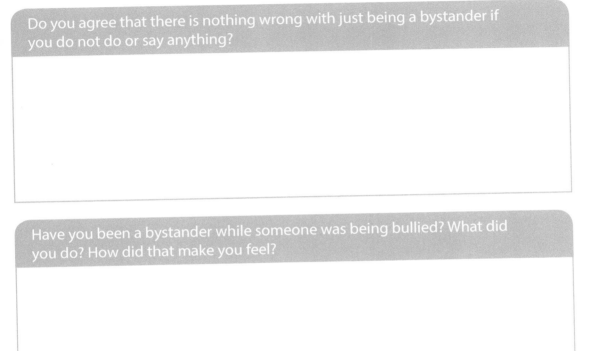

Do you agree that there is nothing wrong with just being a bystander if you do not do or say anything?

Have you been a bystander while someone was being bullied? What did you do? How did that make you feel?

As a bystander, one can feel guilty, have empathy, be desensitized, or indifferent to the feelings of the victim or the bully.

Why do bystanders stay bystanders?

- Afraid of becoming a target for the bully
- Afraid of getting hurt themselves
- Feel that intervening will make the situation worse
- Do not know what to do
- Lack of coping skills themselves
- The bully is their friend

- It is not my problem
- She/he (victim) is not my friend
- Feels they deserve to be bullied
- Do not want to be called a snitch
- Do not want to be an outcast (stay in the in-group.)

BYSTANDER EMPOWERMENT ROLE

When the bystander is no longer the bystander:

It is also common for the bystander to sometimes encourage or join in with the bullying.

Note: *When this happens, the bystander is no longer a "bystander," they are now the "bully" as well.*

Another common problem that happens with bystanders is that they often participate in the spreading rumor(s) or what happened. Today, everyone wants to record incidents (good and bad) and be the first one to post it on social media. Some things are posted without even verifying the truth before posting. But even if it is true, the Sufis Wisdom saying, "Our words must pass through three gates before we speak," would be wise to implement before you post it or share it with someone.

But what are the three gates that the Sufis Wisdom quote speaks of?

1. Is it true?

⮑ If it is not, do not says it is
⮑ If it is, it must go through more gates

2. Is it necessary to say?

3. Is it kind?

Key Point: *It is a bad habit to put yourself in a position where no one shares information with you because you are not trustworthy. So be careful of always being the one that "has to tell it."*

3.5 | Different Bullying Situations/Roles

What do I do if I am being bullied?

What do I do if I am the bully?

What do I do/not do if I know someone is being bullied?

You never know when the situation may present itself (if it has not already), and if the situation does occur, what will you do? What should you do?

Hopefully, this workbook will help you learn the skills needed, so you will be ready to help yourself or help someone else from a bullying situation. Remember, I told you earlier that bullying is not only a childhood problem, but it also happens in adulthood as well. So, the skills/habits you are forming will stick with you, and they will be the same skills you will most likely use when you are an adult.

Things to Do if you are Being Bullied

- Ask the bully to stop
- Tell a teacher
- Walkaway
- Talk to the counselor
- Count to 10 before responding or reacting
- Talk to a trusted friend
- Use assertive skills
- Avoid being alone with the bully
- Believe in yourself.

Things to do if "YOU" are the Bully

First: STOP!

Second: Get Help! (counselor/mentor/parents)

People do not think about this, but the bully needs help just like the victim. Bullies in childhood tend to escalate and become bullies in adulthood. Sometimes children that bully have been bullied themselves. It can occur within the home from parents, siblings, as well as from friends and within the community.

Bullies may have feelings of being inadequate in an area of their life, and this is what leads to that feeling of wanting to exert power over the ones they bully.

Often bullies are also battling with low self-esteem, feeling unloved, and poor social skills.

Have you ever heard the term "hurt people, hurt people"? So, bullies need just as much help as their victims to learn the "why" of their pain. There is always a "why." We do not often want to face the "why" of things because it can be painful and shameful, but that is what needs to happen.

If you are the bully, helpful tips that you need to know:

- Learn and understand your feelings
- Understand the consequences of your actions
- Learn and understand the impact bullying has on the victim
- Find other outlets if it is a need for power-seeking
- Learn/practice self-discipline
- Learn/practice empathy for others (how would you feel if you were them.)

Remember: *There is always a "Why" no matter what position you are in.*

Things TO DO if you know someone being bullied

Some suggestions to do to help someone if you know they are being bullied. "Be a Buddy"!

You may know someone that is being bullied or have been bullied. The following is some key thing that you can do that will help.

- Assure you believe them
- Let them know they are not alone
- Affirm that it is not their fault
- Help them learn things that they can do
- Help them develop a plan to a trusted adult to report the bullying.

Things NOT TO DO if you know someone being bullied

- Do not minimize the bully's behavior (not a big deal)
- Do not rationalize the bully's behavior (make excuses)
- Do not encourage them to bully back
- Do not encourage them to confront the bully
- Do not ("you") confront the bully
- Do not try and solve the problem for them, make sure the victim is part of the process in planning (to the trusted of their choice.)

"Cowardice asks the questions: is it safe?
Expediency asks the question: is it political?
Vanity asks the question: is it popular?
But conscience asks the question: is it right?
And there comes a time when one must take
neither safe position, nor politic, nor popular--
but one must take it because it is right."

Martin Luther King

We have talked about bullying from different roles. You never know when the situation may present itself (if it has not already), and if the situation does occur, what will you do? What should you do? So now, we are going to add what you should do to maintain a healthy positive attitude state of mind (coping skills) into the workbook. Bullying, anger, and any other adverse event/situation can affect your mood in an unhealthy way.

The next sections will go over different coping skills that help with many challenges in life and bullying. These coping skills are not only useful with bullying, but you will apply them to many difficult, troublesome areas of life.

I encourage you to practice learning coping skills or write them down and carry them with you, whatever it takes for you to know them, or have them when you need them. So, as you go through this workbook, the coping skills you like, can relate to, or find useful, jot them to memory, put them in your phone so you can have them when you need them. Stay ready, so you do not have to get ready!

3.6 Coping Skills for Bullying Situations

Coping skills are techniques and tools used to help you handle difficult emotions, situations, stress, etc. and maintain a good sense of internal order.

In plain terms, feel good about yourself, inside and out. If you learn and develop good coping skills, they will help you through difficult times in life. This means that when things are in chaos around you, you will be able to find a way to remain in a good, calm place during the chaos (good mental health.)

I encourage you to learn coping skills for different situations before you experience the situation. Why? Because most of the time, when the situation arises, if you do not already know some coping skills, there is no way you can use what you do not have. I am going to used the statement I said earlier, "If you stay ready, you don't have to get ready,"

Within this section, we will go over the following coping skills

- Understand "Your" Emotions
- Being Assertive
- "I" Statements
- Passive vs. Aggressive Behavior
- Bill of Rights for Everyone
- Change your surroundings
- Have a Positive Support Team?

Coping Skills are used as a "conscious" effort to solve personal and interpersonal problems to decrease or to tolerate stress and conflict better. "Coping" is the strategies and "skills" is the application of the approach.

Coping skills can be good and bad. The goal is for coping skills to decrease stress. However, sometimes using coping skills can make the situation worse (increase your stress instead of decreasing.)

When we positively use coping skills, they help us get through difficult times, which is important for our mental and emotional health.

> Do you think coping skills are important? If so, why, and what are some coping skills you feel you currently have?

One of the first things you should do is to understand your emotions first. So, before we go any further into this section, let us stop here and see how you feel today.

> How do you feel? Why do you feel the way you do? What happens? Give a brief description.

How many times have you acted out without thinking? Have you heard people say, "he/she was acting out of emotions?" I know I have been guilty of doing this. Then later, think to myself, "why did I do that, or why did I say that?"

There are a lot of different emotions/feelings, and we can experience more than one emotion at a time, which complicates things.

List all the emotions you can think currently of at this moment, just by name, for example: happy, sad. etc....

Some emotions are stronger than others, which makes them harder to control. Anger, for example. Some people have a harder time controlling anger than others.

The key is to learn how not to let your emotions control you. As we learn to understand our emotions, we will begin to stay in control of them, and it is not always easy. One way this is accomplished is by using coping skills.

For you to take control of your anger, you have to change the negative thoughts of thinking it's impossible. The first step is to start thinking positive. The next step is to learn your feelings, accept your feelings, and practice strategies to help you deal with your feelings in a hopeful and healthier manner.

Do not think that using a definite coping skill will always make the situation feel good or turn out the way you expect or want the situation to turn out. Coping skills help you deal with the situation in a healthy way and increases the chances of you responding in a healthy way, but it doesn't mean you will like the outcome or always feel good about the healthy positive decision you made.

Think of a time when you were experiencing more than one emotion at the same time. What was the situation and described the feelings you experienced? What was the outcome?

What emotions are most challenging to you, and why?

Assertiveness

Being **assertive** simply means that you are able and willing to speak up for yourself in a firm, calm manner with respect to other opinions and thoughts.

Learning how to be assertive is not only an important skill for coping with bullying, but learning how to be assertive will help you with all situations in life. Assertiveness is also a skill that, once you learn, you will be more effective in communicating with others and resolving conflicts at home, in school, at work, and within the community.

Assertiveness enables people to act in their own best interests, to stand up for themselves, to express honest feelings comfortably, and to express personal rights without denying the rights of others.

People commonly confuse being assertive with being aggressive. They are not the same. **Aggressive** behavior is when people attract or ignore other people's opinions in favor of their own.

Key Point: When being assertive, it's the utmost respect for others' thoughts, feelings, and beliefs without ignoring

our own.

Assertive Characteristics/Traits:

- Speaks to the point
- Speaks openly
- Makes good eye contact
- Expression match the message
- Relaxed open posture
- Participates in groups
- Values self-equal to others
- Tries to hurt no one including themselves
- Usually reaches goals without alienating others.

When Assertive Communication is Properly Used

- The rights of all parties involved are respected (empathetic)
- One's needs are met, while also promoting respectful relationships
- Appropriately asks for and obtains what you need, while preserving relationships (basically no one leaves mad or feels disrespected)
- Use of a calm tone
- Avoids labels and judgments
- "Asks" rather than "demands."
- Values herself and values others equally
- Uses "I" statements to get the message across
- Does not exaggerate the situation
- Sticks to the facts.

Some Key Assertive Skills for the Role of Victims in Bullying:

- Respond to insults/teasing with a bland nonchalant response such as, "Oh, that's just your opinion." It takes away the feeling of power that bullies sometimes thrive. So, not letting the bully see that they have upset you may deter the Bullying because it is no longer fun for them.
- Leave the situation if you start to get angry.
- Learn to firmly say, "No" to things that someone wants you to do, and you do not want to do it.
- Stand up straight and look the person in the eye (be direct and confident)

- Do not let others talk you into doing something that you will be sorry for later (do not fall into the "I dare you" trap.)
- Tell parents and adults that you are being bullied. I know this is hard as people (not just children) do not want to be labeled as a "snitch" or "tattletale."

Key Point: *Tattling is different from telling. Tattling is done when you want to get someone in "trouble." Telling is creating a safe environment for the victim. Telling can also prevent another student from being bullied.*

General Strategies for Assertiveness:

- Look confident by standing tall and holding your head up
- Do not cry and runoff: move closer, turn sideways, and make non-threatening eye contact
- Keep your facial expressions neutral. Do not look sad, and do not look angry.
- Hold your arms beside your body. Do not hold your arms up like you want to fight or have them crossed like you are mad.
- Make your positive comment and then walk off confidently.

Assertive communication is hard for most people, as it is not often naturally obtained. It is more of learned behavior that affects everyone, even adults, as well as children. I know you may have said and heard this before, "When I get grown, I will..." The truth of the matter is these habits that you have today will be the same habits you'll portray when you become an adult (both positive and negative.)

Understanding assertive skills are necessary because, more often than not, people let others walk all over them rather than speak up for themselves. Then the person that has been walked on feels angry, hurt, and often takes it out on themselves or someone else that did not cause the pain. Have you ever heard the phrase, "Don't be anyone's doormat?" That is sort of what happens when you do not stand up for yourself. The lack of this skill is a common cause of anger because remember the definition of anger (perceived threat, violated, hurt.)

Some examples of assertive strategies for bullying situations that the victim or bystander may use:

- **Make an assertive statement** such as "Stop it!" Make it with a serious face but with a calm voice. Do not whine!

- **Fogging**- (admit the characteristic) soft verbal comebacks. For example, if someone says your fat, you can respond, "You're right, I need to lose some weight."

- **Admit the obvious** - point out that the bully sees the obvious, "Wow, he/she noticed I'm fat."

- **Broken record** - Repeat, "What did you say?" or "That's your opinion," or "So."

- **Expose the ignorance** of the bully. For example, if you are being bullied because of a medical problem or disability, tell him the facts about it.

- **Give permission to tease**. "Well, it's ok to say what you want. It doesn't bother me."

- **Use a sense of humor**. For example, the bully says, "You sure do have big ears." You could say, "I know, sometimes I feel like an elephant!"

- **Make an asset** of the bullied characteristic. For example, if you are teased about losing hair because of an illness like cancer, you can say, "Well, I guess Michael Jordan and I are alike, we both don't have that much hair."

Key Point: *When being assertive, you are commiting to repect and reconized other people dignity.*

"I" Statements

"I" statements are a great way to explain your feelings, and what effect the situation or behaviors has on you.

It keeps the other person from becoming defensive, thus shutting down or becoming argumentative.

Examples of "I" statements:

- "I feel disrespected when you say you are coming and don't show up."
- "I feel uncomfortable when you make plans without talking to me first."
- "I feel anxious when you say you will call me, but don't."

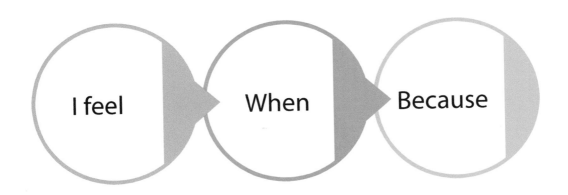

Can you identify the parts? What are they?

I feel_____

When_____

Because_____

Passive Characteristics/Traits

Passive characteristics/traits are responding in a way that gives in to the wishes of others and not thinking of or taking into consideration how you feel.

Some people choose the passive response because of a strong need to be liked or accepted by others. The rights, wishes, and feelings of others are thought of with the hopes to please them. For example, saying yes to someone or something when you want to say no.

Examples of Passive Characteristics/Traits

- Easily intimidated by others
- Avoids eye contact
- Appears shy
- Difficulty telling people no
- Does not stand up for themselves
- Intimidated by authority
- Rarely gets what they want or need
- Does not state their opinions
- Isolates from people groups

- Agrees with others despite their feelings
- Values themselves less than others.

Aggressive Characteristics/Traits

Aggressive characteristics/traits are responding in social interactions with someone or others with the intent of inflicting damage or hurtful things upon another individual.

Examples of Aggressive Characteristics/Traits

- Ignores the feelings and rights of others
- Believes that their rights, opinions, or needs are more important than others
- Violates the rights and boundaries to get what they want
- Demanding
- Angry/hostile
- Exaggerates the facts
- Alienates others
- Interrupts and "talks over" others
- Speaks loudly
- Glares and stares at others
- Uses expression to intimidate others
- Controls people/groups
- Considers own feelings only
- Makes demands of others.

Three different situations are directly associated with you being assertive.

1. How to say "NO" to unfair or unreasonable requests.

2. How to make a reasonable request to others.

3. How to express your feelings.

Key Point: *Assertiveness is the balance point between passive and aggressive.*

Passive	Aggressive	Assertive
Afraid to speak up	Interrupts and talks over others	Speaks openly
Speaks softly	Speaks loudly	Use a conversational tone
Avoids looking at people	Glares and stares at others	Makes good eye contact
Shows little or no expression	Intimidates others with an expression	Shows expressions that match the message
Slouches and withdraws	Stands rigidly, crosses arm, invades others personal space	Relaxes and adopts an open posture and expression
Isolates self from groups	Controls groups	Participates in groups
Agrees with others, despite feelings	Only considers own feelings or own demands	Speaks to the point
Values self-less than others	Values "self" more than others	Values "self" equal to others
Hurts self to avoid hurting others	Hurts others to avoid being hurt	Tries to hurt no one-including self
Does not reach goals and may not know goals	Reaches goals but hurts others in the process	Usually reaches goals without alienating others

Do you see yourself as being assertive, passive, or aggressive? It is not uncommon to see yourself as all three in different situations. But which one applies to you the most and why?

A small overview of assertive before going into the next section.

Behaviors that Identify Whether you come off as Assertive:

- Strong, confident tone (not too loud or too soft), even-toned
- No hesitating or fumbling over your words
- Good eye contact, not staring
- Facial expressions matching what you are saying, relaxed, caring, smile
- Body position-stand straight, do not slouch, erect but relaxed, shoulders straight
- Distance-stand about 3 feet away from the person (too close can cause them to be uncomfortable.)

Things that may interfere with your assertiveness skills:

- Handing over your power: this is the use of the "You make me" statements. "You make me mad." "You make me sick." No one can make you feel anything. You are the Owner of Your Feelings! When you begin the conversation with, "You make me..." it often puts the other person on the defensive as soon as they hear those words.

- Making Judgments: Don't assume things. Make sure you have all the facts before you make a judgment.

- Applying Labels: When you put labels on people, they often begin to defend themselves. When this occurs, it may prevent the original meaning of the conversation from being heard.

- Over-generalizing: This happens when you use the word always. For example, "You're always late."

- Finding fault: "It's not my fault...." makes the other person feel as if you are blaming them. Once again, the the message becomes lost as the person becomes defensive (usually instantly).

- Failing to empathize: "I can't understand why you're always late." A good rule to practice is to put yourself in the other person's shoes before you speak/act.

We all Have Rights

As American citizens, we all have rights.

Every Person's Bill of Rights

- The right to be treated with respect
- The right to have and express your feelings and opinions
- The right to be listening to and taken seriously
- The right to set your priorities
- The right to get what you pay for
- The right to make mistakes
- The right to choose not to assert yourself
- The right to say NO without feeling guilty.

The last one, the right to say no. Individually, we forget that one. As selfish as we can be in human nature, it is not uncommon to have difficulty for most of us to say those two letters: N-O.

Why Should you Learn to say "NO"?

You cannot do everything, and you should not put your feelings and rights aside because you are unable to say no to something. The key to learning how to say no is first to understand why you are saying no.

Learning to Say No as an Assertive Technique:

No is a small yet powerful word. This small word can cause a lot of negative consequences and ruin relationships if not used effectively and productively. The first key in learning to say "no" is understanding why you are saying no. Sometimes it is not about the no, but how you say no.

Often times it is hard to stand up for yourself as a child or adult. That is why learning how to be assertive is important. The lack of assertive skills often plays a huge part in whether a person becomes the victim of Bullying. One way of being assertive is developing boldness within to say no, which is a tough thing to do.

We have all been in a situation where we wanted to say no but could not, or had a hard time doing so. Sometimes we will say no, only to have someone talk us out of "no." There are times when it's hard for anyone to say "yes," but we will focus on the "no" for right now.

Learning how to effectively say no will help you stay in control of your time and life. It does not mean that you are selfish or uncaring. Learning to say no means effectively you care enough about yourself, as well as caring about the feelings of others.

So, as you read this section, Remember Key Points of "NO":

- Is not a dirty word
- You can say no without feeling guilty
- No can increase the value of things you mean
- You have every right to say **No**!

Why do we find it hard to say, No?

- We want to be helpful (a nice person even though it will drain our time or take away from what we need)
- We want to be liked (we do not want to look like we are difficult)
- We do not want to burn bridges (sometimes telling someone no can burn bridges or end relationships, so we do not preserve the relationship)
- We do not like or want conflict (avoids confrontation)
- We do not want to be rude (as a child we are sometimes taught saying no is being rude.)

Key point: *Saying no is a skill that can be learned.*

Steps in Learning to say "No":

- Ask yourself, "Is the request reasonable?"
- Pay attention to your body cues (hesitation, nervousness, tightness in your body, uneasiness)
- Assert your right to ask for more information and clarification before you answer
- Once you understand the request and decide you want to say no, firmly, and calmly say, "No."

Helpful Tips for Saying "No":

- Be direct
- Be assertive; look confident
- Prepare and practice before having the conversation
- Have a support person present
- Use humor when appropriate
- Avoid uncomfortable or dangerous situations (some situations you can avoid if you stay away from them
- Leave if someone is not taking no for an answer and keeps pressuring you. It is best to leave, so you do not give in. If you continue to say no, a conflict may arise.

Assertive Ways of Saying "No":

- Keep answers clear, brief, firm, and honest
- Begin the answer with the word "no," so it is not doubtful
- Make your answer short and to the point
- Do not give a long explanation
- Be honest, direct, and firm
- Do not say, "I'm sorry, but."

Helpful Techniques to Understand When Saying "No":

- It is your right to say, "NO!"
- You deny your importance when you say yes and mean no
- Saying no does not mean you are rejection another person, you are simply refusing a request
- When you say no, it is important to be direct, concise and to the point
- When you say no, do not be swayed by pleading, begging, compliments, or any other form of manipulation
- Offer a reason for your refusal, but do not get carried away with numerous excuses
- Keep apology simple, to avoid offensive excessive apologies
- Demonstrate assertive body language.

> Why do you think assertiveness is important? Describe a time when you were assertive. What was the outcome? What happened if you were not assertive?

Remember: *Assertiveness is not only a matter of what you say but also a function of how you say it! Sometimes having additional information to give along with what you say is helpful because our natural tendency is, we want to explain why.*

When you need informative ways to say no (a little help):

The following are some examples of informative ways to say no that may be helpful for you when you feel the desire to give details of why you are saying no. I have to admit. I am guilty of this sometimes. I feel like I have to explain sometimes why I am saying no. For some reason, it just makes me feel better. So, if you are this type of person, you are not alone.

Examples of informative ways to say NO:

❶ **Direct No** - commonly used when you lack the time or will to do something. Example: "No", I can't pick you up tomorrow because I have other plans tomorrow."

❷ **Reflecting No** - acknowledging the content and feeling. Example: "I know you were counting on me to pick you up, but unfortunately, I can't."

❸ **A Reasoned No** - giving a brief and genuine reason for saying no without opening the situations up for negations. Example: "No, I can't pick you up. I have to work at the same time."

❹ **The Broken Record No**- this is used when someone is constantly asking while the other is repeatedly saying "NO".

❺ **The Pain Now or Pain Later No**- "I would pick you up, but I'm not sure how my schedule will look tomorrow."

❻ **The No Sandwich**- this is a way to give a nice "no." It is when the "no" is from a situation of "yes-no-yes" (sandwich b/c no is in the middle). The relationship is affirmed by the first yes, then you give the no to the request, followed by thanking them for asking you. Example: "Yes, I could pick you up, but not this time. Thanks for asking, and I may be able to pick you up next time."

❼ **The Yes If No**- also known as the negotiator's no. Here you set the conditions of when you can do it. Example: "Yes, I can help pick you up if you let me know two days in advance."

❽ **The Delayed No**- "I'll let you know tomorrow after I check my work schedule."

Build a Positive Support Team

Have you ever heard "misery loves company" or the term "pity-party"? These are two examples of a support team that is not positive. They may be supportive because they are feeding your negative actions. You need a support team that will provide you with honest and healthy advice, rather than someone one to feel sorry for you.

Your support team should listen to you objectively and provide feedback if needed. But remember, sometimes just having someone to listen to is enough. You do not always have to have someone respond to you. The fact that you have gotten the words out of your head will make you feel better. "Put it in the air."

Now, this goes both ways. You cannot expect people to be there for you, and you are never there for them. You should also be talking to "your" team during the good times in your life before you find yourself needing them for help. No one wants to feel used. Some examples of support teams may include family, friends, teachers, mentors, role models, counselors, therapists, or members of a church.

Do you have a support team? If so, who? If not, who might you start to seek out to build your support team?

Change Your Surroundings

It does not mean you can just move out of the house if parents were the first thing to come to mind. However know that there are some modifications in your surroundings that can help your overall mood. These changes can be big or small.

For example, removing negative people from your life who put you down or who are always talking bad about people. Do not hang out with them or listen to their negativity. I know you might think that since you are not saying these negative things that it does not affect you, but it does. Have you ever heard anyone say, "Don't be a garbage can" or "If you put good in, you will get good out?" Even as a teen, you can avoid going to certain places that you know are not positive for you. I know there are many times I will get off the phone or leave a situation if I feel it is not suitable for my mental health.

What are some places, people, situations that you can avoid that may hurt your emotions/feelings?

Section 4

Conflict Resolution

"Don't ever let them pull you down so low as to hate them."

Booker T. Washington

4.1 | Conflict

Conflict is natural part of life that occurs daily at some point.

Every time you interact with someone, there is a possibility that conflict can occur. Why? Everyone needs and expectations are not always the same. Some conflicts are our own (internal), and we displace them onto others because we do not know how to deal with conflict effectively. We disagree with ideas or behaviors, not people, which is difficult because we sometimes have trouble understanding or communicating how we feel.

Some General Concepts about Conflict:

- Is a fight, battle or struggle, strife, controversy, or argument
- Based on one's interpretation of the situation (impartial view)
- Caused by issues associated with differences in cultures, values, beliefs
- Inevitable Change (it will happen)
- Occurs moreover perceived differences than real ones
- Handled differently by everyone
- A part of life needed for growth and maturity
- Affected by our natural internal responses (emotions)
- Peer Pressure/Stress are factors.

Places/People Where Conflict May Occur:

- Classroom/school
- With siblings
- With friends
- With family
- Within the community
- In the world.

How do you define conflict?

Name a conflict you currently have or have had in the past. How did you deal with this conflict? Was it resolved, if so, how? How did you feel?

Three Main Types of Conflict:

- Personal/Relational- internal (inside you/identity) or with different aspects of relationships (confidence broken/loyalty/respect/trust)
- Conflict of Interest- affected by beliefs/values of how certain things are perceived/achieved/agreed upon
- Instrumental- disagreements of structures, goals, events, or processes.

Negative Associations with conflict:

- Fight
- War
- Hate
- Hit
- Push
- Argue
- Wrong or no solutions are possible.

Positive Associations with Conflict:

- Talking
- Listening
- Cooperating
- Sharing
- Everyone has feelings of respect
- Everyone's ideas are understood
- Good solutions are possible.

Conflict is a part of everyday life that everyone experiences at some point.

There is no way to prevent conflict totally, but you can learn ways to avoid conflict or cope with conflict in a positive, productive way. It is important to learn how to deal with conflict and how to respond to it. The overall concept is that people are not in agreement with something. This disagreement causes feelings of stress, frustration, anger, or resentment. Bullying often occurs from "unresolved conflict."

You have your personal beliefs, values, and interpretation of things, and everyone has their own beliefs, values, and own way of interpreting things as well. Everyone is not affected in the same way about the same thing. We all grow up in different homes/environments where we learn and develop values and beliefs from our surroundings.

Conflict often happens when someone does not see things the same as we see them. The difference in perception is what causes conflict. How many times have you spent trying to get someone to see things the way you do? Understand your point of view? Change their mind?

Conflict will happen, and it does not start when you become an adult. You have already had many conflicts in your life at your current age.

> Name a conflict you have had in the past. How did you deal with this conflict? Was it resolved, if so, how? How do you respond to conflict?

Conflicts occur when the basic needs of a person are not met. It could be one basic need or all of them. So, what are the basic needs?

Basic Human Needs:

- ➲ Safety/Security (free from fear, anxiety, stability in life)
- ➲ Belonging/love (acceptance by others, strong personal ties with family, friends, and identity groups)
- ➲ Recognition (need to be recognized as strong, competent, and knowing you influence your environment)
- ➲ Personal fulfillment (need to reach your goals/visions in all areas of your life)
- ➲ Identity (sense of self-recognized by others/throughout the world)
- ➲ Freedom (need to exercise choice in all aspects of one's life)
- ➲ Justice (need for fairness/respect and just division of resources
- ➲ Fun (enjoy life, pursue enjoyment and recreation.)

Describe some things you do to meet your basic needs in the areas listed below.

Safety/Security

_____
_____
_____
_____

Belonging/Love

_____
_____
_____
_____

Recognition

_____
_____
_____
_____

Personal Fulfillment

_____
_____
_____
_____

Identify

_____
_____
_____
_____

Freedom

_____
_____
_____
_____

Justice

_____
_____
_____
_____

Fun

_____

_____

_____

_____

Conflicts can also occur from not having enough of something. For example, not enough:

⮌ Money

⮌ Time

⮌ Food.

Scenario: If there are only one ball and two students, both are crying, want the ball. How can this conflict be resolved?

| O | Often | S | Sometimes | N | Never |

?	O	S	N
Yell or threaten people			
Avoid or ignore people			
Change the Subject			
Try to understand others point of view/ side			
Complain to an adult			
Call people names			
Let other people have their way			
Let an adult decide who is right			
Apologize			
Hit or push people			
Make a joke out of everything			
Try to reach a compromise in disagreements			

4.2 | Conflict Resolution

Conflict happens! We cannot avoid conflict all our life. Conflict can be positive or negative. When conflict is managed and dealt with early, there is less stress and tension with those involved in the situation (which makes it good). Before you can resolve any conflict, you must understand what the conflict is and where the conflict is coming from.

Conflict Arises From:

- Different beliefs/values between people
- Interpersonal
- Stress
- Change (inevitable -will happen)
- Peer pressure
- Emotions (our natural response can cause a conflict.)

So, what happens when there is a conflict, or should I say, what should happen? Ideally, we want the conflict resolved, right? However, that does not always happen. Some people think with time, conflicts can be resolved, and there is some truth to that. However, sometimes even after time has passed, the conflict still lingers and grows and must be resolved for healthy relationships and situations.

If you learn to deal with conflict effectivley, it possible to get positve outcomes. When conflict is dealt with negatively, thigs can escalte quickly and lead to physical and emotional violence. It is important to learn how to deal with conflict and how to respond to conflict.

So, what does conflict resolution mean? The goal of conflict resolution is to resolve the conflict without hurting others and developing a plan/agreement both parties can live with/get their needs meet.

Answer the following questions.

1. Does avoiding or ignoring a friend who you are mad at help to solve the problem? Are you getting your needs met? Why, or why not?

2. Does letting another person have his or her way (i.e., if you are silent and do not say anything about how you feel) help you resolve conflict? Why, or why not?

3. Does calling someone names to help you resolve conflicts? Why, or why not?

Different ways you can respond to conflict:

- Confrontation
- Denial/Avoidance
- Collaboration/problem-solving
- Compete or fight
- Compromise
- Smoothing over the problem.

All are common and used differently by everyone. There is no one specific answer to how conflict can be resolved, and there are no absolutes. You may use more than one within the same conflict. Everything depends on the people involved (goes back to beliefs, values, emotions, etc.)

Confrontation- happens a lot, and it can be positive or negative. You can confront people without yelling, cursing, hitting, etc. But most of the time, when we think of confrontation, it is with yelling cursing, hitting, etc.

Denial/Avoidance- Act as nothing has happened. It is also common, but what happens when you keep all your feelings inside and not communicating (letting the other person know there is a conflict) is not always right. Think of the coke bottle effect if you shake it up over and over. Eventually, it will explode. When it explodes, it goes everywhere, and you cannot control where it goes, how far it goes, or whom it affects. This strategy can be helpful if you or the other person needs time to "cool down" before talking, or the conflict is unimportant. In that case, avoidance may be a win-win. However, this may be a lose/lose situation if the conflict needs to be resolved, and it is not.

Collaboration/Problem-solving- Classic win/win situation. It requires that input be received and considered from all that is involved. It is not as common, but if done the right way, the results are more productive. Problem-solving means you are working with the person you disagree with. It does not mean that any one person has to "win" the disagreement; it just means that you and the person in the disagreement are talking things out. Sometimes it is a win-win, win-lose, or lose-lose at the end of problem-solving. However, both parties have gotten their feelings out and usually will not walk away mad or vowing never to speak to that person again.

Compete or Fight- Classic win-lose situation where one person may use strength, power, or knowledge over another person to win.

Compromise/Negotiation- Not a win/win, more like a draw. You and the person that you conflict with each agree to give up something. Try to find another way.

Smoothing over the problem- AKA "faking it." On the surface, things appear to be fine, but underneath (deep down), there is still conflict. It may be useful if it is more important to save a relationship, but both of you must feel this way. If one person wants to "fake it" and the other does not, it creates a win-lose situation. Just keep in mind this would be a short-term solution that could create problems in the long run.

Remember:

- Win-win: both side's needs are met
- Win-lose: one side's needs are met
- Lose-Lose: no one's needs are met

(lose-lose almost always occurs when confrontation is used as a strategy.)

Benefits of Conflict Resolutions

- **Peace of Mind**- How many times have you relived a conflict or thought about it over and over in your mind? Why? Because it bothers you that it was not resolved. Even if we do not get the answer or expected outcome, it is peaceful to walk away, "knowing that you know" and not wondering "what if."

- **Closeness with Others**- People like it when they connect with someone. When conflict is resolved, both parties tend to know what is going on with each other and have a more personal feeling in the relationship.

- **Healthy**- Unresolved conflict tends to lead to stressful thoughts that can linger for days or even years. Stress is unhealthy for the body and can lead to ulcers, headaches, poor self-esteem, etc. (the list is endless.)

Barriers to Conflict Resolutions

Common Barriers that Stop Conflict from Being Resolved:

- **Communication**- What you say/what you do not say/how you say because if the person does not understand the message you relay, they would have to guess. How many times have you walked away from a conversation, wondering, "What in the world?"

- **Different views (beliefs/values)**- Some people have firm, uncompromising beliefs about how to do things that could stop a conflict from being resolved.

- **Cultural differences-** Your values, perceptions, attitude, and beliefs make up your social being. It is what you use to decide if something is normal, if you agree with something, how and what you will accept. When respect for other cultures is not given while communicating with someone, this creates a barrier in communication as everyone wants respect.

- **Change/transitions-** We like predictable, secure patterns in our life. When things change suddenly or without enough time for us to process our thoughts, needs, and feelings, conflict may occur. Even if the change is positive, there may still be some annoyance, anxiety, and confusion.

- **Coping Skills (ineffective)-** Coping skills are things you do when you are trying to solve a problem, change something, or express disagreement with something. When you do not use positive effective coping skills, this creates a problem in communication. Anger and frustration are normally the first go-to when there is a lack of coping skills while communicating.

- **Leaving Things Unsaid:** Silence alone says different things that may or may not be interpreted correctly. It may be "I don't care, I don't know, I can't deal with this right now," or even incur feelings of shame, guilt, or doubt. By not saying anything, the listener must guess or assume what you meant. Silence leaves a grey area for the listener to have to speculate what your true message is. Remember, we all have different views, so what you "meant" might not be interpreted correctly.

- **Leadership or decision making (lack of or ineffective)-** There are times when you will have to decide on things. When you cannot, and the communication process is negatively effective because nothing will be resolved.

Communication

Communication is sharing information or making something familiar to all those involved in the exchange of information from one place, person, or group to another.

"People fail to get along because they fear each other; they fear each other because they don't know each other. They don't know each other because they have not communicated with each other."—Martin Luther King Jr

For communication to occur, there must be one sender, a message, and a recipient.

The goal of communication is to be understood as the speaker and to understand the messenger. Sounds so easy, but of course, by now, you have probably figured out for yourself that "effective" communication with positive results can be hard.

Communication is complex because you have two or more people trying to understand each other without losing themselves in the process of the conversation. Each person is trying to get their point in and often too busy trying to talk that they are not really listening to what is being said.

The different ways that we use to communicate:

- Verbal
- Non-verbal
- Written
- Visualizations (graphs, charts, etc.)

Things that can influence the way we communicate with others:

- Age
- Gender
- Race
- Socio-economic status (education, income, occupation)
- Education level
- Physical restraints (hearing difficulties)
- Emotions.

Communication has two parts:

The speaker and the listener(s)

1. The message is clearly expressed by the speaker
2. The listener(s) clearly understand the message as the speaker intended.

We will briefly go over some things that positively and negatively affect communication skills.

These things include:

- Tone
- Body language/ Facial expression
- Non-verbal cues
- Feedback.

Tone- It should match what the speaker is saying. If you are saying something nice, you would not be yelling and screaming.

Body language- Standing up straight and making good eye contact are ways that your body will let the speaker know if you are paying attention.

Facial expression- Make sure what you say matches the expression on your face. For example, you would not be smiling when you are angry with someone.

Non-verbal cues- Poor eye contact, gazing into outer space, playing on your phone. I have had people tell me they can multi-task, and this may be true, but it does not present a clear picture that you are listening to me. The person talking should always have the listener's undivided attention. If you must answer a call, text, or ask to be excused for a minute, do not just do it while they are talking.

Feedback- Either ask a question for clarity or paraphrase what you heard as the listener, so the speaker knows that you understood the message that was relayed.

Key Points:

- *Improving your communication skills will help you clearly understand the message that other people are saying.*

- *You are learning and knowing better communication skills will also help you to make sure that other people are understanding you when you are talking.*

- *Good communication skills may help to reduce levels of frustration, anger, and disappointment.*

Basic Tips for Good Communication:

- Use questions that will encourage the listener(s) into further discussion
- Give the speaker your full and undivided attention
- Allow the speaker to finish their statements before you respond
- Do not focus on concluding, focus on listening
- Do not finish what you think the speaker is trying to say
- Do not assume, ask for clarification
- Rephrase what you heard to check for mutual understanding.

Communication Exercise

Describe a situation you have been in that you did not say anything or what you said was not clear? Was there a conflict?

Describe a situation where you did not receive their message clear (they did not say anything, or it was not clear to you). How did you feel?

Describe a time when "how" something was said (tone, body language, non-verbal cues) affected the message given or how the message was understood. It can be done by you or by someone else. What was the outcome?

Interpersonal Conflict

- The conflict between two or more people
- We all do not agree or see things the same. The way we are raised greatly influences our beliefs and values.

Beliefs/Values

- What influences your perceptions of beauty, justice, morals (what is good or bad?)
- Your decision-making process and your methods of reaching your goals are developed by your underlying values
- Affects what you say and do
- They are expressed by your preferences, opinion, beliefs, culture, and personality.

Personal Prejudice

- It is "our opinion." How we feel about something is not always the same as how others feel about things, which could cause conflict.

Key Points to Remember and Use When you have a Difficult Conversation with Someone:

- *Make sure you have all the information you need and the facts straight.*

- *Be assertive*
- *Have empathy- put yourself in the other person's shoes and think about how you would feel if the roles were reversed.*
- *Prepare to negotiate (win-win is beneficial to everyone, so do not always have the mindset that you just have to win at all cost)*
- *Use appropriate nonverbal and verbal communication*
- *Speak clearly (do not use jargon because the other person might not understand you and start assuming what you meant)*
- *Avoid negative body language*
- *Listen*
- *Stay calm and focus.*

Difficult Characteristics in People:

Some people have some characteristics that no matter how hard you try will be challenging to talk to or resolve conflict. Remember, it is the characteristic and not the "person" that is difficult. Characteristics can be changed, learned, and unlearned.

Often, we just reconcile it to "the person" and feel hopeless or negative about that person and shut down or do not talk to them anymore. But if you recognize these characteristics and practice effective conflict resolutions, there is a high chance the problem may be resolved, understood, or respected without bitter feelings or damaging the relationship forever.

Key Point: *You cannot change people. But if you recognize certain characteristics or traits, you may make different choices decisions since you are better informed.*

Know-it-alls

- They know everything
- No patience for letting other people talk

Do not be intimidated or let them take over the conversation. Listen and try to benefit from their knowledge (if it is useful.)

Victims

- It is never their fault
- Always complain of being treated unfairly.

Do not become their protector. Ask them for suggestions that you may be able to help them improve the situation. This will help them practice giving positive thoughts instead of negative thoughts.

Sarcastic

- Will use words as a weapon to destroy the peace.
- Poor team players.

Do not let them talk down to you, be assertive and direct to let them know you will not accept the sarcasm. As hard as it is, do not join them. If they say something in a helpful, productive way, compliment them for saying something positive.

Nay-sayers

- Have nothing good to say about other people or different ideas of others

Do not try to reform them. Ask them to offer suggestive alternatives (this usually makes them stop because it is asking for something positive.)

Yay-Sayers

- Goes along with everybody
- Often for approval.

You may have to stop them from making more commitments than they can handle or just agreeing to everything.

Aggressive:

- Forces point of view on others
- Attacks verbally.

Do not attack back. Be assertive and ask them to talk calmly. Sometimes, if you are not reactive, it diffuses the situation.

Withdraws:

- Does not have anything to say or does not want to contribute to solving the conflict
- Do not pressure them to open up. Try using open-ended questions and have patience.

Management Styles of Conflict Resolution

Conflict can be difficult for everyone regardless of age. It is normal to not want to end up in a win-lose situation, which normally happens when someone feels as if they do not have an equal footing in a relationship.

Key Point: We all have choices. If you pick a choice and you do not like the end results, you can always make another choice.

In conflict, we all have to make an individual choice of how we will handle the conflict.

Common Choices We Can Make During a Conflict:

Choice #1: Acceptance/Accommodation- We decide to fully accept the circumstances and its outcome, although I am, or I may be giving up a lot to accept it. We embrace it with our minds and welcome it into our reality. Highly effective if all parties are honest and agree with the decision.

Choice #2: Change- We can change the situation and alter it to make it more bearable. We may not be able to change the situation but may have to change our approach to the situation to make it more bearable.

Choice #3: Leave- Also can be looked at as a withdrawal. Sometimes, in a situation is so unbearable that to accept or to change the situation feels impossible. To protect ourselves, we leave the situation, and it may be the best solution. Leaving may be temporary or permanent. That is a situational choice that we have to make individually.

Choice #4: Giving in- Rather than confronting the conflict, we concede. This is a passive approach that some people do out of fear or maybe just seeking approval. It is an ineffective approach and usually leaves feelings of one-sidedness, low self-esteem, lack of self-love, and manipulation. No effective solutions are made, and a feeling of submission, resentment, and hopelessness can arise within the person who gives in.

Choice #5: Blame- This will lead to a relationship and anger of one or all parties involved. Ineffective because it is manipulative and unfair. Over time, hostility may occur.

Choice #6: Denial/Avoidance- Is the problem that big/serious? Will you be miserable if you leave it alone and walk away from it? This is one of the least preferable choices because the situation is not fully accepted, no change has been made. Basically, no one wants to "rock the boat." However, it is still an option that is available. Quite often, most people pick #4 to avoid conflict with hopes that it will go away on its own. Unfortunately, it does not, so this is usually an infective approach.

Choice #7: Compromise- Is trying to find a fair, optimal solution for everyone involved in the conflict. This is when those involved want to create or maintain a healthy relationship. Everyone controls their anger, competitive feelings, and passive and aggressive impulses. They work to genuinely find mutually acceptable solutions. "I'll give a little, and you will give a little."

Choice #8: Aggression- Someone decides they will win the conflict at all costs. There may not be a consideration for emotions or how the relationship will be affected. They may "play dirty" and say things that are not true or hurtful in order to win. Their mindset is that of, "I will win!"

Choice #9: Problem Solving- Everyone agrees to discuss things openly and honestly to find a solution that will benefit all parties involved.

You may have already developed a common conflict solution for yourself that you will commonly use. You may use them all at some point or use certain ones more than often than you use others. We commonly use different conflict resolutions with different people.

After reading the different types of conflict management/resolution styles, which styles do you feel commonly used now?

Write about a frustrating situation or conflict that you recently found yourself in. What was the outcome?

What were the available choices that you had to pick from? Was there a positive or negative impact from that choice?

Conflict Resolutions Principles Overview

1. Joint Effort/Mutual Satisfactions

The goal of conflict resolution should be to have a positive, productive outcome for both parties. This is best achieved when all parties consider issues to be mutual and collaborate on a resolution that will benefit both.

2. Problem Definition

The problem should be defined so that all parties have a clear understanding of the issue being addressed. Problems should be focus specific and limited in scope (not too broad and all over the place.)

3. Problem Resolution

Once the problem resolutions have been initiated, all parties should remain focused on the issue defined. No other issues should be introduced, nor should the issue under discussion be redefined.

4. Change First

Each partner should be willing to make changes in his/her behavior first without expectations/insisting that he/she will change when his/her partner changes first.

5. Listen and Validate

The feelings that one is being listened to and taken seriously may be more important than winning.

6. Conflict Resolution Should Reflect a Negotiated Compromise

Success should be mutual.

Key Point: *Conflicts are solved when there is a willingness to let go of being right, of being defensive, and of being in control.*

Choose the best answer.

1. The first step in the conflict resolution process is:

    a. Telling the other person how we should solve the problem

    b. Stop, calm down, and regroup

    c. Deciding who was right

    d. Talking about the problem on Facebook

2. It is important to:

    a. Make sure I do not get in trouble because of a conflict

    b. Be accountable for poor choices I have made and apologize when I am the wrong

    c. Never back down

    d. Tell my friends what the other person did wrong when there is a conflict

3. When trying to resolve a conflict:

    a. I must listen to the other person and consider his or her point of view

    b. I should always just let the other person have their way, so there is no problem

    c. It is not important to talk about my feelings

    d. It is ok to ignore the other person's ideas if I do not like them

4. To make conflict resolution productive:

    a. I should get it over with as quickly as possible

    b. Everyone involved should just ignore their feelings

    c. One person should be happy with the solution

    d. I must focus on the issue and stick to the facts

Write down your ideas for possible solutions for the following conflict scenarios:

_____

_____

_____

_____

_____

_____

_____

1. A friend says something means about you on Facebook.

2. Your brother borrowed your iPod charger, and now it is broken.

3. You find out one of your friends had a party and did not invite you.

4. A friend took your phone and started reading your texts.

5. Your sister will not let you change the channel to watch your favorite show on TV.

Effective Keys for Conflict Resolutions:

Keep in mind; you will be doing group projects in High School and College with peers. These steps will come in handy.

1. Find OK-ness Within Yourself.

- Before you attempt to resolve a conflict, stop and take a few deep breaths.
- Give yourself time to think, time to be reasonable, logical, and rational.
- What is important to you in the conflict? Be truthful with yourself.
- This is a great time to figure out your emotions. What are you feeling, and why?
- You may need to take time to cool off until you understand and have dealt with your emotions.

2. Recognize Conflict Issues.

- When a conflict arises, it will be helpful for you to recognize it as a conflict and accept the problem as an opportunity to seek an understanding of yourself and the other participants.
- Think of it as a time for maturity and growth.
- Remember that each participant's attitude will influence the formation of a solution.
- Brainstorm and understand what the true issues of the conflict are from all parties involved.

3. Select an Appropriate Time and Place to Discuss the Issues.

- Pick a time that will allow for mutual respect and comfort for everyone.
- Do not pick a time when you or the other person is tired, hungry, emotionally upset, rushed for time, or at an inappropriate place (i.e., public restaurant)
- If you must, postpone the discussion until the conditions are better.

4. Treat Each Other with Respect.

- Behaviors (verbal and nonverbal) give a reflection on if a person is getting or receiving respect.
- The way people look at each other, their word selection, whether they are

listening or not, and tone will come across as respectful or disrespectful.

- Be careful of name-calling or labeling.
- Keep the conversation in the present not in the past (example "you always.")
- The golden rule, "Do unto others as you would want them to do unto you."

5. Listen carefully

- During the conflict, feelings are often intense, and communication is difficult.
- Thoughts, feelings, and needs of all participants need to be heard.
- Listening to someone makes them feel that you have taken them seriously.
- Listen until you experience the other side. Listening is not merely "hearing."

6. Focus on Feelings

- An important thing to remember is to control your emotions first.
- You can only control your emotions
- It is also important for you to understand and respect the emotions of the other participant you conflict.
- The resolution of a conflict will be hard, if not impossible, until all parties know and understand the other party's feelings regarding the conflict.

7. Verbalize Conflict Issues.

- Words are powerful and can make or break the situation.
- Be real. It does not help to withhold important information or talk about one thing when the situation is really about another thing.
- State what you believe without getting angry or being dramatic.
- Tell your feelings. If you are angry, say that you are angry, but in a positive effective way because until emotional issues are acknowledged, conflict resolution will be difficult.
- Communicate what is true for you.

8. Identify Your Share of the Problem.

- Make sure you accept your responsibility for the problem because the willingness and admittance of your part in the conflict will influence the other participants to cooperate.

- This will help with creating an open, inviting discussion for everyone to discuss their personal acceptance of the conflict.

9. Recognize and Identify Optional Solutions

- Being able to recognize and identify a solution that will work for all parties
- Solution(s) should not be where a participant leaves angry, sad, or hurt
- More than one solution to be decided upon is beneficial
- The more options you have, the better chance of finding one that will work for all participants (win-win.)

10. Choose a Mutually Acceptable Solution.

- To effectively become, a choice must be made at some point.
- Make sure all options are evaluated
- Mutual respect is given in picking a solution
- Determine the steps of implementing the solution
- Determine what is required from each participant. Keep in mind of how all parties will be affected.

Helpful Questions to Ask Before any Attempt of Conflict Resolution

- Is the problem worth the effort to resolve it?
- Will talking about these issues improve our relationship?
- Am I willing to spend the necessary time and energy talking about the issue and help the other person by listening?
- Have I chosen an appropriate time and place for this confrontation?

Note: *If the answers to the helpful questions are all or mainly "yes," then continue with the ground rules to resolve the conflict.*

If most of the answers are "no," you may need to try a different way of expressing your concerns. For example, you may decide to share your feelings without problem-solving.

Common Ground Rules in Conflict Resolution:

- One person speaks at a time
- Mutually agree to listen to one another
- Try to under the other person's perspective of the situation before responding
- Agree to maintain confidentiality (do not gossip and tell others)
- If others need to know, decide together, and have a clear understanding of who else needs to know
- Agree to communicate openly, respectfully, and directly with each other
- Agree not to attack each other's character personally.

What is the overall message you received concerning ways you should/
should not use to solve a conflict with someone?

Additional Exercises/Reflecting questions:

What did you learn about the topic of bullying?

How do you think being bullied makes people feel?

Section 5

Self-Control

"*To handle yourself, use your head; to handle others, use your heart*"

Eleanor Roosevelt

5.1 | *Self-Control*

When you control your actions/feelings and do not present or have some type of unwanted behavior, that is self-control.

All behavior is learned, and this includes your response to anger. If you have negative responses to things, you can turn the negative responses into positive responses.

Many Things can Cause us to Lose Control of Ourselves

- Anger
- Criticism
- Untruths said about us
- Lack of sleep
- Personal conflict
- Bad mood
- Personal/Physical things.

One way to have control over yourself is to know yourself. I know I have said this a few times, but the first step is recognizing your anger triggers and cues. Sometimes, we do things so often and for so long that we feel it is natural who we are, or we do not realize we are doing it. It is not healthy to "swallow" (ignore) our anger or let it go unresolved.

When it comes to self-control, we have two choices we can act upon:

1.   We respect the rights of others.
2.   We ignore the rights of others.

Respecting the Rights of Others- when we respect the rights of others, it keeps the relationship healthy and builds stronger relationships. Respecting the rights of others will also allow you to get more support from others.

- Listening
- Having Empathy
- Finding ways to resolve anger
- Forgiving.

Stepping on the Rights of Others- stepping on the rights of other damages or ends our relationships with others. It also causes people not to want to support us.

- Yelling
- Using threats of violence
- Blaming
- Shutting down (silent approach-not talking to someone)
- Holding a grudge (refuse to find a way to resolve the issues.)

As soon as you recognize your triggers, this is when you should take the opportunity to take some control and remind yourself to calm done. This can be done with a coping skill known as "self-talk."

> What are some areas in your life that you need to improve self-control?

> Describe a situation you lost control of yourself. How did you feel? What was the outcome?

5.2 | *Self-Talk*

"Self-Talk" is things that you silently tell yourself. This is normally done internally (in your head.)

If you talk to yourself, it may be done externally. The main thing is it is the things that you tell yourself and normally the things we tell ourselves that we do not share we others.

Normally, we use self-talk in a negative way.

Key Point: *"The only thing you can control is you and your response." Changing your thinking from negative to positive is an excellent way to get better with learning useful anger management techniques.*

Examples of Self-talk Cues that You Can Tell Yourself When You Start Feeling Angry:

- Relax
- Calm down
- Stop
- Do not do it.

Negative Self-Talk

This is when you criticize yourself or blame others for your problems. Negative self-talk can add to your anger and make it harder to effectively handle your anger.

When you use self-talk as in a positive manner, it is a GREAT coping skill! You are telling yourself great things about you. You are encouraging you. Who better to tell you good things about you than you?

This can be one word or short snappy sentences used to remind you that you need to calm down and decrease your levels of anger. Understanding "self-talk" is a way to help you recognize negative things that you tell yourself and change them to positive thoughts that can help decrease anger (make you feel better.)

Positive Self-Talk/Self-Affirmations

- The first step is to stop the negative self-talk as soon as it gets into your head. Replace the negative thought with a positive one.

Example: If you tell yourself, "I can't handle this." You can stop this thought and say, "Relax, I can handle it."

- Tell yourself these things daily or when you are in a difficult situation (the more you hear it, the more you will believe it)
- Make sticky notes and put them around your room, in folders, and places you will see them daily
- Write them over and over.

I believe in journaling and self-help logs. It is a great way to help you focus and self-reflect. It helps you keep up with the changes you have made or need to make. I also feel that when you put things down on paper, it is also a way to hold yourself accountable when you see it.

Example of Positive Self-Talk/Self-Affirmations Statements

- I am confident
- I am competent
- I am respected
- I am admired
- I am a kind and loving person
- I contribute to the world
- I matter
- I can deal with conflict
- I can handle anger
- I can deal with stress
- I will the best I can be
- I am committed to being healthy, happy.

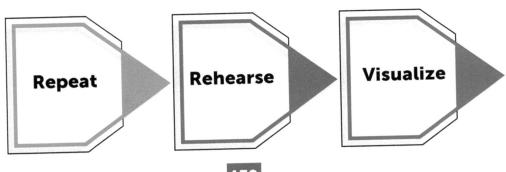

Repeat → Rehearse → Visualize

Taking Action

Self-Talk Log

Now It is time to write down several problems or situations that have made you angry, and you said or had a negative thought. Then write a positive thought for that same situation.

Keep track of your thoughts over the next couple of days.

Situation	Negative Thought	Positive Thought

What other "self-talk" cues can you think of that you can use?

CONGRATULATIONS !

You have taken the steps to read "Greater Than My Mood" First Edition Guide for Anger, Anger Management, Bullying, Conflict Resolution, and Self -Control.

I hope that you have enjoyed the lessons and techniques I have provided for you to utilize in your life everyday. Remember, when facing challenges in, you are "GREATER THAN YOUR MOOD!"

Ramona,

NOTES

Glossary

A

Active Listening- A communication process in which the listener uses nonverbal behaviors, such as eye contact and gestures, as well as verbal responses, including tone of voice, open-ended statements, restating, and summarizing, to demonstrate to the speaker that the listener is paying attention.

All or Nothing Thinking- You see things as black and white with nothing in between. You are either right or wrong, smart, or stupid. You have difficulty seeing alternatives, which could lead to an angry response.

Ally- When a person is on the same side as someone in a situation.

Avoidance- The practice of non-engagement.

B

Bias- A preconceived opinion or attitude about something or someone. A bias may be favorable or unfavorable.

Body Language- Posture, body positions, and looks while listening and speaking that reveal additional information about how we feel and what we are thinking.

Bully- When you scare or threaten someone with words or actions.

Bystander- A person who watches an event or situation but does not participate in the case.

C

Catastrophizing- When a small incident feels like a disaster. Example: You spill a drink on the carpet, and you go on and on about it in an extreme manner. (I am so careless, now I must spend time cleaning it. It might not come clean. The stain will not come out, and the carpet ruined)

Clarify- To make clear or to enhance understanding. During a conflict-resolution procedure, open-ended questions used to clarify meaning.

Closed Questions- Questions that answer with a simple response such as "yes" or "no" and do not give the receiver (listener) very much information.

Conflict- An expressed struggle between at least two interdependent parties who perceive incompatible goals, scarce resources, and interference from the party in achieving their goals; a controversy or disagreement; to come into opposition.

Conflict Resolutions- A spectrum of processes that utilize communication skills and creative thinking to develop voluntary solutions that are acceptable to those concerned in a dispute.

Culture- A part of human interactions and experiences that determines how people feel, act, and think. Through learning, one establishes the standard to judge right from wrong, lies, and truth, and the worth of oneself and others. It is dependent upon nationality, ethnicity, race, genders, sexual orientation, socioeconomic background, ability, and age.

D

Disability- A mental or physical condition that places unique challenges on a person.

Discrimination- Treating someone different because they are not in the same category of race, religion, gender, or sexual orientation.

Disqualify the Positive- Anything positive about you, or anything positive that happens is discounted. For example, if either he/she apologized, but may have done something wrong in the first place.

Diversity- A combination of people sharing the same background.

E

Empathy- When you feel or know how/what someone else feels (usually because you have experienced the same thing).

F

Filtering- When you only look at the bad, never the good in yourself and others.

Fortune telling- You think you know what will happen next and get angry based on that assumption.

G

Gender- How a person identifies with their sexuality.

Gender Role- Society's expectation of gender roles.

Gender stereotype- "Fixed" ideas about how males and females are "supposed" to act.

H

Harass- To repeatedly bother or upset someone else with words or actions.

Hate crime- Threatening attack (usually physical) on someone because of different beliefs or different views.

Hot thoughts- Angry thoughts that pop in your head and make you feel angrier about the situation.

Humiliate- Make fun of someone, cause them to feel less of a person.

I

"I" Statements- Way of expressing ourselves when we are using our "active listening" skills that take responsibility for our feelings and express our needs. The use of "I" statements are used to try and deescalate the conflict and promote healing communication.

Interests- A substantive, procedural, or psychological need of a party to the conflict; the aspect of something that makes it matter to someone else.

L

Labeling- You "label" external triggers in a way that will promote an angry response. Example: labeling someone as an "idiot." Now every time you see this person, you have little tolerance for that person.

M

Mediation- A process that allows people who have a conflict with each other to discuss things in a structured environment that facilitates a peaceful resolution that is fair to everyone.

Mindreading- You think you know what will happen next and get angry based on that assumption.

N

Negotiate- Working to find a suitable answer compromise for all parties involved. The goal is to find a way to satisfy everyone.

O

Overgeneralization- One adverse event is the beginning of a never-ending pattern. Ex: if you experience anger the first time, you will get angry every time.

Open Questions- Questions that prompt the person being asked to offer more information, which can help the listener understanding how they are feeling or thinking.

P

Position- A point of view or a specific solution that a person (party) proposes to meet his or her interests or needs. A position is likely to be concrete or explicit, and often includes demand or threat that leaves little room for discussion. In conflict resolution, it is essential for participants to get beyond "their" positions and to understand their underlying interests and needs.

Prejudice- An opinion about someone without knowing if it is accurate or knowing them as a person.

Personalization- If something wrong happens, you think/feel it must have been your fault. You feel all your causes are ignored. Alternatively, you could interpret actions and behaviors as being directed at you specifically.

Pro-social Behavior- Learning or reinforcing skills for getting along with others.

R

Resolve- To settle a conflict or disagreement through a process such as mediation.

Resolution- The actual details of the settlement of a conflict or disagreement.

Respect- Appreciate or admire someone through positive words or positive behaviors.

Rumor- Is information about someone that is spread to others, often without the person's consent. It can be true, false, or exaggerated.

S

Shared Interest- Something the parties can agree on or something they both want that can become the starting point of a possible agreement to a conflict.

Slur- Disrespectful or inappropriate word used with the intent of putting someone else down.

Stereotype- Description of someone based on an inaccurate assumption about a whole category of people.

T

Target- Person being bullied by others.

Tolerate- not being upset or bothered by other people's differences.

Trust- to have confidence in or to feel sure.

V

Value- a principle, standard, or quality considered worthwhile or desirable.

Violence- the unjust or abusive use of power; force exerted to injure, damage, or abusing people or property.

Meet the
Author

Ramona Girley
PMHNP

She is a Registered Nurse for over 25 years who is currently working as a Psychiatric Mental Health Nurse Practitioner, where she sees children and adults in an outpatient setting. Ramona founded a nonprofit organization, RG MindfulHealth 4 OUR Youth Inc., to give back to the community (particularly the youth).

She was born in Little Rock, AR, and moved to Mississippi in the military which she served six years active duty in the Air Force at Keeler Air Force Base. She is a wife, a mother of four children, two grandchildren, and expecting several grandchildren soon.

MINDFULHEALTH
4 OUR Youth

About RG MindfulHealth 4 OUR Youth

RG MindfulHealth 4 OUR Youth is a nonprofit agency that provides mentoring programs for middle and high school youths in Gulfport, Mississippi, and the surrounding communities. The organization's goal is to foster a commitment to youths that will promote pro-social friendships and strong interpersonal skills and help them reassert a sense of hope in the future.

Research has proven that through personal relationships, a sense of individual responsibility will be reestablished that will give youths the commitment to follow through on a path to adulthood with a sense of pride and accomplishment. Through repeated failures in the home, school, and communities, and the development of destructive habits, youths often lose faith in the possibilities that await them if they can successfully put their life together. This goal is better accomplished when youths are in a caring, inclusive-learning environment that promotes their best effort and reinforces personal respect.

RG MindfulHealth 4 OUR Youth is a direct response to the growing number of youths that are being bullied, thinking of self-harm, and diagnosed with cognitive disorders. The goal of the program is to mentor youths who are having a turbulent transition from adolescence to adulthood and offer positive support to avoid the pitfalls that can derail their lives. This age group (middle school and high school) is particularly problematic and a perfect time for mentoring to be effective.

The organization's focus is different from the usual youth programs for decreasing teen pregnancy, decreasing gang violence, and preventing school dropouts. Still, the goal remains the same: empower youths to make a positive change in their lives.

RG MindfulHealth 4 OUR Youth was founded by Ramona Girley, a Psychiatric Mental Health Nurse Practitioner (PMHNP) and Registered Nurse who has worked with children and adults with psychiatric mental disorders. The organization is also supported by qualified professional volunteers who share the same goals, visions, and purpose of empowering and transforming youth to become the best they can become.

RG MindfulHealth 4 OUR Youth Inc.
1526 Mills Ave Room 14
Gulfport, MS 39507
228-265-9804

References

Chance to Change. The Greatest Hero.
Retrieved from:https://c2ctoolbox.eu/2018/10/09/the-greatest-hero/

Dombrowski, Ruth .Anger Management Workbook
Retrieved from https://seasonstherapy.com/wp-content/uploads/2013/12/
What-Causes-Anger.pdf

Everyone Bill of Right.
Retrieved from:https://www.mhankyswoh.org/Uploads/files/pdfs/
ConsumerRights-EveryonesRights_20130813.pdf

(2009, May 20). HealthyPlace Mental Health Newsletter, HealthyPlace.
Retrieved on 2020, August 1 from https://www.healthyplace.com/other-info/
mental-health-newsletter/index

IREX Conflict prevention and peer mediation toolkit 15; Glossary
Retrieved from:https://www.irex.org/sites/default/files/node/resource/
conflict-resolution-and-peer-mediation-toolkit.pdf

Let us Get Real Curriculum Guide
Retrieved from: https://www.groundspark.org

Learning to say "No". Positive People.
Retrieved from:http://www.easetheload.com/images/pdf_files/learning-to-
say-no.pdf

Olweus, D. (1993) Bullying in School. What we know and what we can do.:
Oxford, UK: Blackwell Publishers. https://positivepsychology.com/

Pfeiffer, Rich(2019, 20 October) Anger Management Workbook and
Curriculum. Retrieved by:http://www.growthcentral.com/wp-content/
uploads/2014/08/Anger-Management-Workbook-and-Curriculum.pdf

Wright, Jim (2017) Preventing Classroom Bullying: What Teachers Can Do.
Retrieved from: http://www.interventioncentral.org

Suicide and Depression Awareness for Student.
Retrieved from:https://www.learnpsychology.org/suicide-depression-student-
guidebook/

Credits

Publisher
Gemlight Publishing LLC

Photography
David Pittman
DP Photography LLC

Editor
Nicole Dentremont

Interior Design
Elac Taghap

Cover & Book Design
Erica T Sherrill

Illustrations
All vector art illustration by Freepik.

CPSIA information can be obtained
at www.ICGtesting.com
Printed in the USA
BVHW021503300721
613263BV00018B/1096

9 781734 432688